500 FREE
DAYS OUT

Produced by AA Publishing

Editorial: lifestyleguides@theAA.com

Front Cover Photos: (top) AA/James Tims; (middle) AA/Tom Mackie; (bottom) AA/George Munday

All photographs in this guide: 1 AA/John Wood; 3 AA/Neil Setchfield

Printed in China by Leo Paper Products

Directory compiled by AA Lifestyle Guides Department and managed in the Librios Information Management System and generated from the AA establishment database system.

Visit: theAA.com/shop

Published by AA Publishing, a trading name of AA Media Limited whose registered office is Fanum House, Basing View, Basingstoke, Hampshire, RG21 4EA
Registered number 06112600.

A CIP catalogue record for this book is available from the British Library

ISBN 978-0-7495-6458-2

A04301

Welcome to the Guide

This mini guide features 500 places to visit which make no charge for entry. We have included museums, art galleries, national parks, visitor centres, castles and many other kinds of attraction across Britain and Ireland. Entries include contact details, along with a short description, and details of opening times and special facilities. We hope this guide will help you, your family and friends get the most out of your visit.

Contents

Sample Entry

1 LUTON

John Dony Field Centre

Hancock Dr, Bushmead LU2 7SF
2 ☎ 01582 486983 & 422818
e-mail: johndony@luton.gov.uk
web: www.luton.gov.uk/museums
3 dir: signed from rdbt on A6, at Barnfield College
on New Bedford Rd

4 This is a purpose-built study centre for exploring
the landscapes, plants and animals of the
Luton area. Featuring permanent displays
on local archaeology, natural history and the
management of the local nature reserve, it
explains how ancient grasslands and hedgerows
are conserved and follows 4000 years of history
from Bronze Age to modern times. Please contact
for details of special events.

5 Times Open all year, Mon-Fri 9.30-4.45 & for
6 programmed events* Facilities ℗ ℗ toilets for
disabled ⊗

1 Location The directory is arranged in
countries, counties, and in alphabetical
location order within each county.
2 Telephone Numbers have the STD code
shown before the telephone number. (If
dialling Northern Ireland from England use
the STD code, but for the Republic you need
to prefix the number with 00353, and drop the
first zero from the Irish area code).
3 Directions may be given after the
address of each attraction and where
shown have been provided by the
attractions themselves.
4 Description of attraction
5 Opening Times quoted in the guide are
inclusive - for instance, where you see
Apr-Oct, that place will be open from the
beginning of April to the end of October.
✳ Opening times followed by a star relate to
2009. It should be noted that in some entries
the opening dates and times may also have
been supplied as 2009. Please check with the
establishment before making your journey.
6 Facilities This section includes parking, dogs
allowed, refreshments etc. See page 6 for
a key to Symbols and Abbreviations used in
this guide.

How to Use the Guide

Visitors with Mobility Disabilities should look for the wheelchair symbol showing where all or most of the establishment is accessible to the wheelchair-bound visitor. We strongly recommend that you phone in advance of your visit to check the exact details, particularly regarding access to toilets and refreshment facilities. Assistance dogs are usually accepted where the attractions show the 'No Dogs' symbol ⊗ unless stated otherwise. For the hard of hearing induction loops are indicated by a symbol at the attraction itself.

Free Entry The attractions in this guide have told us they do not charge a fee for entry, although they may charge for use of audio equipment, for example. Some of these attractions may ask for or expect a donation.

Credit & Charge cards are taken by a large number of attractions for admission charges. To indicate which do not accept credit cards we have used this symbol at the end of the entry. ▣

Photography is restricted in some places and there are many where it is only allowed in specific areas. Visitors are advised to check with places of interest on the rules for taking photographs and the use of video cameras.

Special events are held at many of these attractions, and although we have listed a few in individual entries, we cannot hope to give details of them all, so please ring the attractions for details of exhibitions, themed days, talks, guided walks and more.

...and finally Opening times and admission prices can be subject to change. Please check with the attraction before making your journey.

Symbols and Abbreviations

Symbols

☎ Telephone number
& Suitable for visitors in wheelchairs
🅿 Parking at Establishment
Ⓟ Parking nearby
☕ Refreshments
🎋 Picnic Area
🍽 Restaurant
⊗ No Dogs
🚐 No Coaches
✳ Opening times relate to 2009
✣ Cadw (Welsh Monuments)
♯ English Heritage
🌿 National Trust
🎗 The National Trust
  for Scotland
▮ Historic Scotland

Abbreviations

BH Bank Hoildays
PH Public Holidays
Etr Easter
ex except
ch Children

6

AMPTHILL

Houghton House

web: www.english-heritage.org.uk
dir: 1m NE off A421

Now a ruin, the mansion was built for Mary
Countess of Pembroke, the sister of Sir Philip
Sidney. Inigo Jones is thought to have been
involved in work on the house, which may have
been the original 'House Beautiful' in Bunyan's
Pilgrim's Progress.

Times Open at all reasonable times.*
Facilities ❷ ✛

BEDFORD

Bedford Museum

Castle Ln MK40 3XD
☎ 01234 353323 📄 01234 273401
e-mail: bmuseum@bedford.gov.uk
web: www.bedfordmuseum.org
dir: close to town bridge and Embankment

Embark on a fascinating journey through the
human and natural history of north Bedfordshire,
pausing briefly to glimpse at wonders from more
distant lands. Go back in time and visit the
delightful rural room sets and the Old School
Museum, where Blackbeard's Sword, 'Old Billy'
- the record breaking longest-living horse, and
numerous other treasures and curiosities can be
found. Housed in the former Higgins and Sons
Brewery, Bedford Museum is situated within the
gardens of what was once Bedford Castle, beside
the Great Ouse embankment. The courtyard and
galleries provide an excellent setting for the
varied collections.

Times Open all year, Tue-Sat 11-5, Sun 2-5.
(Closed Mon ex BH Mon, Good Fri, Xmas & New
Year).* Facilities ℗ ⌁ 🛱 (outdoor) ♿ toilets
for disabled shop 🚫

BEDFORD

Cecil Higgins Art Gallery

Castle Ln MK40 3RP

☎ 01234 211222 📄 01234 327149

e-mail: chag@bedford.gov.uk

web: www.cecilhigginsartgallery.org

dir: in town centre close to Embankment

Bedford Gallery is the completed first phase of the re-development of Cecil Higgins Art Gallery and Bedford Museum. It is a new state-of-the-art exhibition venue which will house varied and exciting exhibitions including touring exhibitions from national museums and galleries.

Times The Cecil Higgins Art Gallery is closed in 2010 for re-development. The new Bedford Gallery in Castle Lane is now open Tue-Sat 11-5, Sun & BHs 2-5. Closed Xmas, New Year & Good Fri. During exhibition changeovers Bedford Gallery will be closed so please check the website for further details. Facilities ℗ ⊟ (outdoor) ♿ toilets for disabled ⊗

LUTON

John Dony Field Centre

Hancock Dr, Bushmead LU2 7SF

☎ 01582 486983 & 422818

e-mail: johndony@luton.gov.uk

web: www.luton.gov.uk/museums

dir: signed from rdbt on A6, at Barnfield College on New Bedford Rd

This is a purpose-built study centre for exploring the landscapes, plants and animals of the Luton area. Featuring permanent displays on local archaeology, natural history and the management of the local nature reserve, it explains how ancient grasslands and hedgerows are conserved and follows 4000 years of history from Bronze Age to modern times. Please contact for details of special events.

Times Open all year, Mon-Fri 9.30-4.45 & for programmed events* Facilities ℗ ℗ toilets for disabled ⊗

LUTON

Stockwood Discovery Centre

Stockwood Park, London Rd LU1 4LX
☎ 01582 548600   📠 01582 546763
e-mail: museum.gallery@luton.gov.uk
web: www.luton.gov.uk/museums
dir: signed from M1 junct 10 & from Hitchin,
Dunstable, Bedford, Luton town centre

Stockwood Discovery Centre is a new museum
and visitor attraction that includes new gardens
featuring world, medicinal and sensory gardens,
a visitor centre with a shop and café selling
locally produced free range products and an
outdoor discovery play area. It also features
fascinating interactive displays about the history
of Luton and the surrounding areas as well as
exciting events and special exhibitions.

Times Open all year; Apr-Oct, Mon-Fri 10-5, Sat-
Sun 11-5, until 8 on 1st Thu of mth; Nov-Mar,
Mon-Fri 10-4, Sat-Sun 11-4.* Facilities 🅿 🅿
🖵 🍴 (outdoor) ♿ toilets for disabled shop ⊗

LUTON

Wardown Park Museum

Wardown Park, Old Bedford Rd LU2 7HA
☎ 01582 546722 & 546739
📠 01582 546763
e-mail: museum.gallery@lutonculture.com
web: www.wardownparkmuseum.com
dir: Follow brown signs from town centre north.
Turn off A6 towards Bedford

A Victorian mansion, with displays illustrating
the natural and cultural history and industries
of the area, including the development of
Luton's hat industry, and the Bedfordshire and
Hertfordshire Regimental Collections. New 'Luton
Life' displays tell the story of the town and its
residents over the past 200 years. Exhibitions
and events throughout the year, please telephone
for details.

Times Open all year, Tue-Sat 10-5, Sun 1-5
(Closed Xmas, 1 Jan & Mon ex BH Mons).*
Facilities 🅿 🅿 🖵 🍴 (outdoor) ♿ toilets for
disabled shop ⊗

STOTFOLD

Stotfold Mill Preservation Trust

Mill Lane SG5 4NU

☎ 01462 734541

e-mail: enquiries@stotfoldmill.com

www: www.stotfoldmill.com

dir: 1m from A1(M) junct 10

In an idyllic setting on the River Ivel, where a mill has stood since the 11th century, this working watermill still produces high-quality stone-ground flour. After a fire in 1992, the Mill was renovated by volunteers who started in 1998, and completed their work in 2006 when the Mill was opened to the public. There are twice-daily guided tours.

Times Open Etr-Oct, alternate Sun (please check website). **Facilities** P 🖵 & toilets for disabled shop ⊗ ex assist dogs ⊚

NEWBURY

West Berkshire Museum

The Wharf RG14 5AS

☎ 01635 30511

e-mail: museum@westberks.gov.uk

web: westberkshiremuseum.org.uk

dir: from London take M4 junct 13, then southbound on A34, follow signs for town centre

Occupying two adjoining buildings in the centre of Newbury; the Cloth Hall built in 1627 and the Granary built in 1720. The museum includes displays of fine and decorative art, costume, local history and archaeology.

Times Open all year Tue-Sat 10-5. Open BH Feb-Nov .* **Facilities** P & (partly accessible) (ground floor accessible) shop ⊗

READING

Museum of English Rural Life

University of Reading, Redlands Rd RG1 5EX
☎ 0118 378 8660 📠 0118 378 5632
e-mail: merl@reading.ac.uk
web: www.merl.org.uk
dir: close to Royal Berkshire Hospital, museum
100mtrs on right

Recently moved to larger premises, this museum
houses a national collection of agricultural,
domestic and crafts exhibits, including wagons,
tools and a wide range of other equipment used
in the English countryside over the last 150
years. Special facilities are available for school
parties. The museum also contains extensive
documentary and photographic archives, which
can be studied by appointment. There is a regular
programme of events and activities, please see
website for details.

Times Open all year, Tue-Fri, 9-5, Sat & Sun
2-4.30 (Closed BHs & Xmas-New Year).*
Facilities ℗ ⩙ (outdoor) ♿ toilets for disabled
shop ⊗

BRISTOL

Arnolfini

16 Narrow Quay BS1 4QA
☎ 0117 917 2300 & 0117 917 2301
📠 0117 917 2303
e-mail: boxoffice@arnolfini.org.uk
web: www.arnolfini.org.uk
dir: From M32 follow brown signs

In a fantastic location at the heart of Bristol's
harbourside, Arnolfini is one of Europe's leading
centres for the contemporary arts. Arnolfini
stages art exhibitions, cinema, live art and dance
performances, talks and events and has one of
the country's best art bookshops. Entrance to the
galleries is free, making Arnolfini a great place to
spend a few minutes or a few hours. The 2 for 1
voucher only relates to cinema tickets.

Times Open all year, Tue-Sun, 10-6 & BHs.
Fees Galleries free, Cinema £6 (concessions
£4.50).* Facilities ℗ 🖵 🍽 licensed ⩙ ♿
toilets for disabled shop ⊗

BRISTOL

Bristol's Blaise Castle House Museum

Henbury Rd, Henbury BS10 7QS

☎ 0117 903 9818

e-mail: general.museum@bristol.gov.uk

web: www.bristol.gov.uk/museums

dir: M5 junct 19, 4m NW of city, off B4057

Built in the 18th century for a Quaker banker, this mansion is now Bristol's Museum of Social History. Set in 400 acres of parkland, nearby Blaise Hamlet is a picturesque estate village, and was designed by John Nash.

Times Open all year: 10-5 Sat-Wed. (Closed 25-26 Dec). Opening hours may change from November 2009 please telephone or check website.* Facilities ℗ 🎠 (outdoor) ♿ (partly accessible) (access ramp, no lift due to age of house) shop ⊗

BRISTOL

Bristol's City Museum & Art Gallery

Queen's Rd, Clifton BS8 1RL

☎ 0117 922 3571 🖷 0117 922 2047

e-mail: general.museum@bristol.gov.uk

web: www.bristol.gov.uk/museums

dir: follow signs to city centre, then follow tourist board signs to City Museum & Art Gallery

Regional and international collections representing ancient history, natural sciences, and fine and applied arts. Displays include dinosaurs, Bristol ceramics, silver, and Chinese and Japanese ceramics. A full programme of special exhibitions take place throughout the year. Ring for details.

Times Open all year, daily 10-5. (Closed 25-26 Dec). Opening hours may change from November 2009 please telephone or check website* Facilities ℗ 🖵 ♿ (partly accessible) (level access entrance, lift to some floors) toilets for disabled shop ⊗

BRISTOL

Bristol's Georgian House

7 Great George St, off Park St BS1 5RR
☎ 0117 921 1362   📄 0117 922 2047
e-mail: general.museum@bristol.gov.uk
web: www.bristol.gov.uk/museums
dir: 5 mins walk from city museum & art gallery

A carefully preserved example of a six-storey, late 18th-century merchant's town house, with many original features, furnished to illustrate life both above and below stairs. Displays allow visitors to examine the role that slavery played in 18th-century Bristol.

Times Open all year: Sat-Wed 10-5. (Closed 25-26 Dec). Opening hours may change from November 2009 please telephone or check website* Facilities Ⓟ ⊗

BRISTOL

Bristol's Red Lodge

Park Row BS1 5LJ
☎ 0117 921 1360
e-mail: general.museum@bristol.gov.uk
web: www.bristol.gov.uk/museums
dir: 5 mins walk from city museum & art gallery

The house was built in 1590 and then altered in 1730. It has fine oak panelling and carved-stone chimney pieces, and is furnished in Elizabethan, Stuart and Georgian styles. The Great Oak Room is considered to be one of the finest Elizabethan rooms in the West Country, and has an original plasterwork ceiling. From here you can look down into the beautiful Knot Garden. The house has been home to many families over the centuries and was a reform school for girls in the 1800s.

Times Open all year Sat-Wed 10-5 (Closed 25-26 Dec). Opening hours may change from November 2009 please telephone or check website* Facilities Ⓟ ⊗

CAMBRIDGE

Fitzwilliam Museum

Trumpington St CB2 1RB
☎ 01223 332900 📄 01223 332923
e-mail: fitzmuseum-enquiries@lists.cam.ac.uk
web: www.fitzmuseum.cam.ac.uk
dir: M11 junct 11, 12 or 13. Near city centre

The Fitzwilliam is the art museum of the University of Cambridge and one of the oldest public museums in Britain. It contains magnificent collections spanning centuries and civilisations, including antiquities from Ancient Egypt, Greece and Rome; sculpture, furniture, armour, ceramics, manuscripts, coins and medals, paintings, drawings and prints.

Times Open all year Tue-Sat 10-5, Sun 12-5. (Closed Mon ex BH, & 24-26, 31 Dec & 1 Jan).*
Facilities ℗ ⚏ 🎋 (outdoor) ♿ toilets for disabled shop ⊗

CAMBRIDGE

Scott Polar Research Institute Museum

Lensfield Rd CB2 1ER
☎ 01223 336540 📄 01223 336549
e-mail: enquiries@spri.cam.ac.uk
web: www.spri.cam.ac.uk
dir: 1km S of city centre

An international centre for polar studies, including a museum featuring displays of Arctic and Antarctic expeditions, with special emphasis on those of Captain Scott and the exploration of the Northwest Passage. Other exhibits include Inuit work and other arts of the polar regions, as well as displays on current scientific exploration. Public lectures run from October to December and February to April. Departure of Captain Scott's Terra Nova from London on 1 June 1910 will be celebrated by the opening of a new Polar Museum on the centenary.

Times Closed for renovation until 1 Jun 2010, then open Tue-Fri 11-1 & 2-4. Sat 12-4. Closed BH wknds, public hols & University hols. Please call 01223 336540 or check the website for further details. Fees Free admission, donations welcome. Facilities ℗ ♿ toilets for disabled shop ⊗

CAMBRIDGE

University Museum of Archaeology & Anthropology

Downing St CB2 3DZ
☎ 01223 333516 ▤ 01223 333517
e-mail: cumaa@hermes.cam.ac.uk
web: www.maa.cam.ac.uk
dir: opposite Crowne Plaza Hotel in city centre

The museum is part of the Faculty of Archaeology and Anthropology of the University of Cambridge. It was established in 1884 and is still housed in its 1916 building on the Downing Site in the city centre. Some of the highlights are Pacific material collected on Captain Cook's voyages of exploration and a 46-foot high totem pole from Canada. Find out about local, national and world archaeology in the Archaeology Galleries, including painted pottery from Peru, giled Anglo-Saxon brooches, and Roman altar stones.

Times Open Tue-Sat, 10.30-4.30.* Facilities ℗ toilets for disabled shop ⊗

CHESTER

Chester Visitor Centre

Vicars Ln CH1 1QX
☎ 01244 351609 ▤ 01244 403188
e-mail: tis@chestercc.gov.uk
web: www.chestertourism.com
dir: opposite St Johns Church Roman Amphitheatre

Among the attractions at this large visitor information centre are guided walks of Chester; World of Names, which explores the history of family and first names; displays on the history of Chester; a café and a gift shop. Chester is the most complete walled city in Britain, and was originally settled by the Romans in the first century AD. The city also played its part in battles with the Vikings, the Norman invasion, and the Civil War.

Times Open all year, Mon-Sat 10-5, Sun 10-4*
Facilities ℗ ⊑ ⊓ (outdoor) toilets for disabled shop

FOWEY

St Catherine's Castle

web: www.english-heritage.org.uk
dir: 0.75m SW of Fowey along footpath off A3082

A small sixteenth-century fort built by Henry VIII to defend Fowey Harbour. It has two storeys with gun ports at ground level.

Times Open at any reasonable time.*
Facilities ℗ ⊗ ♯

SANCREED

Carn Euny Ancient Village

web: www.english-heritage.org.uk
dir: 1.25m SW of Sancreed, off A30

The remains of an Iron Age settlement. Surviving features include the foundations of stone huts and an intriguing curved underground passage or 'fogou'.

Times Open at any reasonable time.*
Facilities ℗ ♯

TRURO

Royal Cornwall Museum

River St TR1 2SJ

☎ 01872 272205 📄 01872 240514

e-mail: enquiries@royalcornwallmuseum.org.uk

web: www.royalcornwallmuseum.org.uk

dir: follow A390 towards town centre

Cornwall's oldest and most prestigious museum is famed for its internationally important collections. Visitors can see large collections of minerals, a real Egyptian mummy and the Cornish Giant. The art gallery has a fine collection of painting from the Newlyn and St Ives Schools, and regular temporary exhibitions of local, national and international artists. The museum runs a range of family activities throughout the year along with a regular programme of lectures. Contact the museum for details of events and activities.

Times Open all year, Mon-Sat 10-4.45. Library closes 1-2, all day Thu & Sat pm. (Closed BHs & Sun). Facilities ⓟ ⊑ 🍽 licensed ♿ toilets for disabled shop ⊗

BARROW-IN-FURNESS

The Dock Museum

North Rd LA14 2PW

☎ 01229 876400 📄 01229 811361

e-mail: dockmuseum@barrowbc.gov.uk

web: www.dockmuseum.org.uk

dir: A590 to Barrow-in-Furness. Follow brown tourist signs

Explore this museum and relive the fascinating history of Barrow-in-Furness. Discover how the industrial revolution prompted the growth of the town from a small hamlet into a major industrial power through models, graphics and computer kiosks.

Times Open mid Apr-Nov, Tue-Fri 10-5, Sat-Sun 11-5; Nov-Mar, Wed-Fri 10.30-4, Sat-Sun 11-4.30.* Facilities ⓟ ⓟ ⊑ 🎋 (outdoor) ♿ toilets for disabled shop ⊗

BROUGH

Brough Castle

CA17 4EJ

☎ 0191 261 1585
web: www.english-heritage.org.uk
dir: 8m SE of Appleby, S of A66

Dating from Roman times the twelfth-century keep at this site replaced an earlier stronghold destroyed by the Scots in 1174. It was restored by Lady Anne Clifford in the 17th century. You can still see the outline of her kitchen gardens.

Times Apr-Sep, daily 10am-5pm; Oct-Mar 10-4. Closed 24-26 Dec & 1 Jan. Please call 0870 333 1181 for details of opening times.*
Facilities ℗ ⊗ ⌗

CARLISLE

The Guildhall Museum

Green Market CA3 8JE

☎ 01228 625241 🖹 01228 810249
e-mail: enquiries@tulliehouse.co.uk
web: www.tulliehouse.co.uk
dir: town centre, behind Tourist Information Centre

Experience the unique atmosphere of the oldest town centre building in the city. The Guildhall was originally a row of shops and workshops attached to a wealthy merchant's town house. It has been owned by the City of Carlisle since the 14th century and is now home to a museum of civic history, such as Carlisle Bells, the oldest horseracing prizes in the country and the impressive medieval monument chest, Victorian civic regalia, and Guild Silver collections.

Times Open Good Fri-Oct, 12-4.30 Facilities ℗ shop ⊗

PENRITH

Wetheriggs Animal Rescue & Conservation Centre

Clifton Dykes CA10 2DH
☎ 01768 866657   📠 01768 866657
web: www.wetheriggsanimalrescue.co.uk
dir: approx 2m off A6, S from Penrith, signed

Wetheriggs is an animal rescue centre with a mixture of farm and exotic animals. All proceeds go towards rescuing and looking after the animals. You can also learn about the heritage of the steam-powered pottery and engine room, and paint your own pot. There is a newt pond, play area and a petting farm and reptile house, café and gift shop, all set in 7.5 acres of the beautiful Eden Valley.

Times Open daily, Apr-Oct 10-4; Nov-Mar 10-3. Closed 25-26 Dec & 1 Jan.* Facilities ❷ ⍁ ☴ (outdoor) toilets for disabled shop

SHAP

Shap Abbey

CA10 3NB
web: www.english-heritage.org.uk
dir: 1.5m W of Shap on bank of River Lowther

Dedicated to St Mary Magdalene, the abbey was founded by the Premonstratensian order in 1199, but most of the ruins are of 13th-century date. The most impressive feature is the 16th-century west tower of the church.

Times Open at any reasonable time.* Facilities ❷ ⊗ ⌗

CHESTERFIELD

Chesterfield Museum and Art Gallery

St Mary's Gate S41 7TD
☎ 01246 345727
e-mail: tourism@chesterfield.gov.uk
web: www.visitchesterfield.info
dir: In town centre

The Museum tells the story of Chesterfield from its beginning as a Roman fort on Rykneild Street to the building of the 'Crooked Spire' Church and its growth as a market town. Chesterfield's most famous Victorian resident, George Stephenson, the 'Father of the Railways' is also featured. The displays continue the story of the town to the present day.

Times Open all year, Mon-Tue & Thu-Sat, 10-4.*
Facilities ℗ ᵬ shop ⊗

DERBY

Derby Museum & Art Gallery

The Strand DE1 1BS
☎ 01332 641901 📠 01332 716670
e-mail: museums@derby.gov.uk
web: www.derby.gov.uk/museums
dir: follow directions to city centre

The museum has a wide range of displays, notably of Derby porcelain, and paintings by the artist Joseph Wright (1734-97). Also antiquities, natural history and a new military gallery 'Soldiers Story', as well as many temporary exhibitions.

Times Open all year, Mon 11-5, Tue-Sat 10-5, Sun & BHs 1-4. Closed Xmas & New Year, telephone for details.* Facilities ℗ ᵬ (partly accessible) (parts of building are not accessible to powered wheelchair users) toilets for disabled shop ⊗

DERBY

Pickford's House Museum of Georgian Life & Historic Costume

41 Friar Gate DE1 1DA
☎ 01332 255363 📄 01332 255277
e-mail: museums@derby.gov.uk
web: www.derby.gov.uk/museums
dir: from A38 into Derby, follow signs to city centre

The house was built in 1770 by the architect Joseph Pickford as a combined workplace and family home. It now shows domestic life at different periods, with Georgian reception rooms and service areas and a 1930s bathroom. Other galleries display part of the museum's collections of historic costume and toy theatres. There is a lively programme of changing temporary exhibitions and events throughout the year.

Times Open all year, Mon 11-5, Tue-Sat 10-5, Sun & BHs 1-4. (Closed Xmas & New Year, telephone for details).* Facilities 🅿 🅿 ♿ (partly accessible) (wheelchair access to ground & lower ground floors) shop ⊗

DERBY

The Silk Mill - Derby's Museum of Industry and History

Silk Mill Ln, off Full St DE1 3AR
☎ 01332 255308 📄 01332 255108
e-mail: museums@derby.gov.uk
web: www.derby.gov.uk/museums
dir: From Derby inner ring road, head for Cathedral & Assembly Rooms car park. 5 mins walk

The museum is set in a re-built 18th-century silk mill and adjacent flour mill on the site of the world's first modern factory. Displays cover local industries, and include a major collection of Rolls Royce aero-engines from 1915 to the present. There is also a section covering the history of railway engineering in Derby. The building is now part of the Derwent Valley Mills World Heritage Site.

Times Open all year, Mon 11-5, Tue-Sat 10-5, Sun & BHs 1-4. (Closed Xmas & New Year, telephone for details).* Facilities 🅿 🅷 (outdoor) ♿ toilets for disabled shop ⊗

OLD WHITTINGTON

Revolution House

High St S41 9JZ

☎ 01246 345727 & 453554

📄 01246 345720

e-mail: tourism@chesterfield.gov.uk

web: www.visitchesterfield.info

dir: 3m N of Chesterfield town centre, on B6052 off A61, signed

Revolution House takes its name from the Revolution of 1688, when this cottage was an ale house - the "Cock and Pynot". It was here that three local noblemen met and began planning their parts in events which led to the overthrow of King James II, in favour of William and Mary of Orange.

Times Open 10 Apr-27 Sep, Fri-Sun & BHs, 11-4.* Facilities ℗ ♿ (partly accessible) (Ground floor access only for wheelchairs) shop ⊗

BUCKFASTLEIGH

Buckfast Abbey

TQ11 0EE

☎ 01364 645500 📄 01364 643891

e-mail: enquiries@buckfast.org.uk

web: www.buckfast.org.uk

dir: 0.5m from A38, midway between Exeter and Plymouth. Turn off at 'Dart Bridge' junct and follow brown tourist signs

The Abbey, founded in 1018, was dissolved by Henry VIII in the 16th century. Restoration began in 1907, when four monks with little building experience began the work. The church was built on the old foundations, using local blue limestone and Ham Hill stone. The precinct contains several medieval monastic buildings, including the 14th-century guest hall which contains an exhibition of the history of the Abbey.

Times Open all year daily. Closed Good Fri & 24-26 Dec.* Facilities ℗ 🖵 🍽 licensed ♫ (outdoor) ♿ toilets for disabled shop ⊗

DARTMOUTH

Bayard's Cove Fort

TQ6 9AT
web: www.english-heritage.org.uk
dir: in Dartmouth on riverfront

Built by the townspeople to protect the harbour, the remains of the circular stronghold still stand at the southern end of the harbour.

Times Open at any reasonable time.*
Facilities ⊗ ♯

EXETER

Quay House Visitor Centre

46 The Quay EX2 4AN
☎ 01392 271611 ▤ 01392 265625
e-mail: quayhouse@exeter.gov.uk
web: www.exeter.gov.uk/quayhouse
dir: Turn off A30 onto A366. Follow signs to historic quayside

Two thousand years of Exeter's history in an audio-visual presentation of the city from Roman times to the present day. Learn about the history of the Quayside through lively displays, illustrations and artefacts.

Times Open all year, Apr-Oct, daily 10-5; Nov-Mar, Sat-Sun 11-4.* Facilities ℗ ♿ (partly accessible) (access to downstairs only) shop ⊗

EXETER

RAMM in the Library

Royal Albert Memorial Museum, Castle St
EX4 3PQ
☎ 01392 665858 📠 01392 421252
e-mail: RAMM@exeter.gov.uk
web: www.exeter.gov.uk/RAMM
dir: off High Street, next to Central Library

With a range of objects on display and hands
on gallery activities, RAMM in the Library is an
ideal place for family visits and to catch up on
news of the Royal Albert Memorial Museum's
redevelopment. Many of the Museum's favourite
activities can be enjoyed here during the closure.

Times Open all year Mon-Sat 10-5. Closed BHs.
Facilities ℗ ♿ toilets for disabled ⊗

LYDFORD

Lydford Castle and Saxon Town

EX20 4BH
web: www.english-heritage.org.uk
dir: in Lydford off A386

Standing above the gorge of the River Lyd, this
tower, dating back to the 12th-century, was
notorious as a prison. The earthworks of the
original Norman fort lie to the south.

Times Open at any reasonable time.*
Facilities ℗ ♯

OTTERTON

Otterton Mill

EX9 7HG
☎ 01392 568521
e-mail: escape@ottertonmill.com
web: www.ottertonmill.com
dir: on B3178 between Budleigh Salterton & Newton Poppleford

Set beside the River Otter in one of Devon's loveliest valleys, Otterton Mill is a centuries-old working watermill, a famous bakery and shop full of local produce, a restaurant, and a gallery of arts and crafts from local artists. Please see website for details of music nights and art events

Times Open daily, 10-5.* Facilities ❷ ℗ ⌂ ◎ licensed ♿ (partly accessible) toilets for disabled shop

PLYMOUTH

Plymouth City Museum & Art Gallery

Drake Circus PL4 8AJ
☎ 01752 304774 🖷 01752 304775
e-mail: museum@plymouth.gov.uk
web: www.plymouthmuseum.gov.uk
dir: off A38 onto A374, museum on NW of city centre, opposite university

The City Museum and Art Gallery runs an exciting programme of exhibitions, talks, concerts, family workshops and other events alongside its gallery collections. There is an interactive natural history gallery and an impressive porcelain and silver collection, as well as the internationally important Cottonian collection. For further details please visit the website. 2010 is the museum's centenary.

Times Open all year Tue-Fri 10-5.30, Sat & BH Mons 10-5. Closed Good Fri & Xmas.* Facilities ℗ ⌂ ⌱ (outdoor) ♿ toilets for disabled shop ⊗

YELVERTON

Yelverton Paperweight Centre

4 Buckland Ter, Leg O'Mutton Corner PL20 6AD
☎ 01822 854250 📄 01822 854250
e-mail: paperweightcentre@btinternet.com
web: www.paperweightcentre.co.uk
dir: at Yelverton off A386, Plymouth to Tavistock road

This unusual centre is the home of the Broughton Collection - a glittering permanent collection of glass paperweights of all sizes and designs. The centre also has an extensive range of modern glass paperweights for sale. Prices range from a few pounds to over £1000. There is also a series of limited edition prints by talented local artists.

Times Open Apr-Oct, daily 10.30-5; 10-24 Dec, daily; Nov & Jan-Mar by appointment.*
Facilities ℗ ♿ shop

CHRISTCHURCH

Christchurch Castle & Norman House

web: www.english-heritage.org.uk
dir: near Christchurch Priory

Set on the river bank, the ruins of this Norman keep and constable's house date back to the 12th-century.

Times Open at any reasonable time.*
Facilities ⊞

CHRISTCHURCH

Red House Museum & Gardens

Quay Rd BH23 1BU

☎ 01202 482860 📄 01202 481924
e-mail: paul.willis@hants.gov.uk
web: www.hants.gov.uk/museum/redhouse
dir: follow brown tourist signs from Christchurch, Red House is on corner of Quay Rd

A museum with plenty of variety, featuring local history and archaeology, displayed in a beautiful Georgian house. There's an excellent costume collection, some Arthur Romney-Green furniture and gardens with a woodland walk and herb garden. Regularly changing temporary exhibitions include contemporary art and crafts, plus historical displays.

Times Open Tue-Sat 10-5, Sun 2-5 (last admission 4.30). Open BHs (spring & summer) Closed 25 Dec-1 Jan & Good Fri.* Facilities Ⓟ 📺 ♿ (partly accessible) (ground floor and gardens accessible) toilets for disabled shop ⊗

DORCHESTER

Maiden Castle

DT1 9PR
web: www.english-heritage.org.uk
dir: 2m S of Dorchester, access off A354, N of bypass

The Iron Age fort ranks among the finest in Britain. It covers 47 acres, and has daunting earthworks, with a complicated defensive system around the entrances. One of its main purposes may well have been to protect grain from marauding bands. The first single-rampart fort dates from around 700BC, and by 100BC the earthworks covered the whole plateau. It was finally overrun by Roman troops in AD43.

Times Open at any reasonable time.*
Facilities Ⓟ ⧉

POOLE

Poole Museum

4 High St BH15 1BW

☎ 01202 262600　📠 01202 262622
e-mail: museums@poole.gov.uk
web: www.boroughofpoole.com/museums
dir: off Poole Quay

After major redevelopment the museum opens its doors again. The museum tells the story of Poole's history, including the Studland Bay wreck and trade with Newfoundland with displays and hands-on activities.

Times Open 6 Apr-1 Nov, Mon-Sat 10-5, Sun 12-5. Closed 25-26 Dec.* Facilities ℗ ▯ ♿ (partly accessible) (Scaplen's Court not accessible) toilets for disabled shop ⊗

TOLPUDDLE

Tolpuddle Martyrs Museum

DT2 7EH

☎ 01305 848237　📠 01305 848237
e-mail: jpickering@tuc.org.uk
web: www.tolpuddlemartyrs.org.uk
dir: off A35 from Dorchester Tolpuddle signed at Troytown turn off. Continue on old A35. From east, the museum has Brown Heritage sign.

One dawn, in the bitter February of 1834, six Tolpuddle farm labourers were arrested after forming a trade union. A frightened squire's trumped up charge triggered one of the most celebrated stories in the history of human rights. That dawn arrest created the Tolpuddle Martyrs, who were punished with transportation as convicts to Australia. Packed with illustrative displays, this interactive exhibition tells the Tolpuddle Martyrs' story. Every summer on the weekend of the third Sunday in July, the museum holds the Tolpuddle Martyrs Festival. The weekend combines celebration with tradition offering traditional and contemporary music as well as many other attractions.

Times Open all year, Apr-Oct, Tue-Sat 10-5, Sun 11-5; Nov-Mar, Thu-Sat 10-4, Sun 11-4. Also open BHs. Closed 21 Dec-6 Jan.* Facilities ℗ ⌂ (outdoor) ♿ toilets for disabled shop ⊗

BARNARD CASTLE

Egglestone Abbey

DL12 8QN
web: www.english-heritage.org.uk
dir: 1m S of Barnard Castle on minor road off B6277

The scant, but charming remains of a small medieval monastery. The picturesque ruins of Egglestone are located above a bend in the River Tees. A large part of the church can be seen, as can remnants of monastic buildings.

Times Open daily, 10-6.* Facilities ❷ ♯

BOWES

Bowes Castle

DL12 9LD
web: www.english-heritage.org.uk
dir: in Bowes village, just off A66

Massive ruins of Henry II's tower keep, three storeys high, set within the earthworks of a Roman fort and overlooking the valley of the River Greta.

Times Open at any reasonable time.*
Facilities ⌂ 🚌 ♯

HADLEIGH

Hadleigh Castle

☎ 01760 755161
web: www.english-heritage.org.uk
dir: 0.75m S of A13

The subject of several of Constable's paintings, the castle has fine views of the Thames estuary. It is defended by ditches on three sides, and the north-east and south-east towers are still impressive.

Times Open at any reasonable time.*
Facilities ⊞

WALTHAM ABBEY

Waltham Abbey Gatehouse, Bridge & Entrance to Cloisters

☎ 01992 702200
web: www.english-heritage.org.uk
dir: in Waltham Abbey off A112

Beside the great Norman church at Waltham are the slight remains of the abbey buildings - bridge, gatehouse and part of the north cloister. The bridge is named after King Harold, founder of the abbey.

Times Open at any reasonable time.*

CHELTENHAM

Cheltenham Art Gallery & Museum

Clarence St GL50 3JT

☎ 01242 237431 🖹 01242 262334

e-mail: artgallery@cheltenham.gov.uk

web: www.cheltenham.artgallery.museum

dir: close to town centre & bus station, 2 min walk from promenade

This museum has an outstanding collection relating to the Arts and Crafts Movement, including fine furniture and exquisite metalwork. The Art Gallery contains Dutch and British paintings from the 17th century to the present day. The Oriental Gallery features pottery, costumes and treasures from the Ming Dynasty to the reign of the last Chinese Emperor. There is also a display about Edward Wilson who journeyed with Captain Scott in 1911-12, together with the history of Britain's most complete Regency town and archaeological treasures from the neighbouring Cotswolds. Special exhibitions are held throughout the year.

Times Open all year, Apr-Oct , daily 10-5; Nov-Mar 10-4 (1st Thu in month open from 11). Closed BHs.* Fees Free, donations welcome. Facilities ℗ 🖵& (partly accessible) (corridor access a bit tight for wheelchairs, some steps) toilets for disabled shop ⊗

GLOUCESTER

Gloucester City Museum & Art Gallery

Brunswick Rd GL1 1HP

☎ 01452 396131 🖹 01452 410898

e-mail: city.museum@gloucester.gov.uk

web: www.gloucester.gov.uk/citymuseum

dir: A38 Bristol Rd to Southgate St, situated between Spa Rd & Brunswick Rd

An impressive range of Roman artefacts including the Rufus Sita tombstone; the amazing Iron Age Birdlip mirror; one of the earliest backgammon sets in the world; dinosaur fossils; and paintings by famous artists such as Turner and Gainsborough. There is something for everyone, full-sized dinosaurs; wildlife from the city and the Gloucestershire countryside; beautiful antique furniture, glass, ceramics and silver; hands-on displays, computer quizzes and activity workstations throughout the galleries. There is an exciting range of temporary exhibitions from contemporary art and textiles to dinosaurs and local history; children's holiday activities and regular special events.

Times Open all year, Tue-Sat 10-5.* Facilities ℗ & toilets for disabled shop ⊗

31

GLOUCESTER

Gloucester Folk Museum

99-103 Westgate St GL1 2PG
☎ 01452 396868 & 396869
🖹 01452 330495
e-mail: folk.museum@gloucester.gov.uk
web: www.gloucester.gov.uk/folkmuseum
dir: from W - A40 & A48; from N - A38 & M5, from E - A40 & B4073; from S - A4173 & A38

Three floors of splendid Tudor and Jacobean timber-framed buildings dating from the 16th and 17th centuries along with new buildings housing the dairy, ironmonger's shop and wheelwright and carpenter workshops. Local history, domestic life, crafts, trades and industries from 1500 to the present, including Toys and Childhood gallery with hands-on toys and a puppet theatre, the Siege of Gloucester, a Victorian class room, Victorian kitchen and laundry equipment. A wide range of exhibitions, hands-on activities, events, demonstrations and role play sessions are held throughout the year. There is an attractive cottage garden and courtyard for events, often with live animals, and outside games.

Times Open all year, Tue-Sat, 10-5* Facilities ℗
🛱 (outdoor) ♿ (partly accessible) shop ⊗

ULEY

Uley Long Barrow (Hetty Pegler's Tump)

web: www.english-heritage.org.uk
dir: 3.5m NE of Dursley on B4066

This 180 foot Neolithic long barrow is popularly known as Hetty Pegler's Tump. The mound, surrounded by a wall, is about 85 feet wide. It contains a stone central passage, and three burial chambers.

Times Open at any reasonable time.*
Facilities 🚻

ASHTON-UNDER-LYNE

Central Art Gallery

Central Library Building, Old St OL6 7SG
☎ 0161 342 2650 📄 0161 342 2650
e-mail: central.artgallery@tameside.gov.uk
web: www.tameside.gov.uk
dir: Near centre of town, off A635 (large Victorian building)

Set in a fine Victorian Gothic building, Central Art Gallery has three gallery spaces, each of which offers a varied programme of contemporary exhibitions. A range of tastes and styles are covered, with group and solo shows of work by artists from the region including paintings, sculpture, installation and textiles. Extensive education programmes for schools, children, families, adults and teenagers.

Times Open all year, Tue, Wed & Fri 10-5, Thu 1-7.30 & Sat 9-4.* Facilities ℗ ♿ toilets for disabled shop ⊗

ASHTON-UNDER-LYNE

Museum of The Manchester Regiment

The Town Hall, Market Place OL6 6DL
☎ 0161 342 2812 & 3710
📄 0161 343 2869
e-mail: portland.basin@tameside.gov.uk
web: www.tameside.gov.uk
dir: in town centre, on market square, follow signs for museum

The social and regimental history of the Manchesters is explored at this museum, tracing the story back to its origins in the 18th century. Children can try on military headwear, experience a First World War trench, and try out the interactive 'A Soldier's Life'.

Times Open all year, Mon-Sat, 10-4. (Closed Sun).* Facilities ℗ ♿ toilets for disabled ⊗

ASHTON-UNDER-LYNE

Portland Basin Museum

Portland Place OL7 0QA
☎ 0161 343 2878 📠 0161 343 2869
e-mail: portland.basin@tameside.gov.uk
web: www.tameside.gov.uk
dir: M60 junct 23 into town centre. Museum near
Cross Hill Street & car park. Follow brown signs
with canal boat image

Exploring the social and industrial history of
Tameside, this museum is part of the recently
rebuilt Ashton Canal Warehouse, constructed in
1834. Visitors can walk around a 1920s street,
dress up in old hats and gloves, steer a virtual
canal boat, and see the original canal powered
waterwheel that once drove the warehouse
machinery. Portland Basin Museum also features
changing exhibitions and event programme- so
there's always something new to see!

Times Open all year, Tue-Sun 10-5. (Closed
Mon, ex BHs)* Facilities 🅿 🅟 🍴 licensed 🍴
(outdoor) ♿ toilets for disabled shop ⊗

MANCHESTER

Gallery of Costume

Platt Hall, Rusholme M14 5LL
☎ 0161 224 5217
e-mail: m.lambert@manchester.gov.uk
web: www.manchestergalleries.org.uk
dir: in Platt Fields Park, Rusholme, access from
Wilmslow Rd. 2m S of city centre

With one of the most comprehensive costume
collections in Great Britain, this gallery makes
captivating viewing. Housed in a fine Georgian
mansion, the displays focus on the changing
styles of everyday fashion and accessories over
the last 400 years. Contemporary fashion is
also illustrated. Because of the vast amount
of material in the collection, no one period
is permanently illustrated. New temporary
exhibitions programme alongside permanent
displays will start in March 2010. Platt Fields
Park celebrates its centenary in 2010.

Times Open from Apr, Wed-Sat 1.30-4.30.
Facilities 🅿 🍴 (outdoor) ♿ (partly accessible)
(stairs with handrails to first floor) toilets for
disabled shop ⊗

MANCHESTER

Imperial War Museum North

The Quays, Trafford Wharf Rd, Trafford Park
M17 1TZ
☎ 0161 836 4000   🖷 0161 836 4012
e-mail: iwmnorth@iwm.org.uk
web: www.iwm.org.uk
dir: M60 junct 9, join Parkway (A5081) towards
Trafford Park. At 1st island take 3rd exit onto
Village Way. At next island take 2nd exit onto
Warren Bruce Rd. Right at T-junct onto Trafford
Wharf Rd. Alternatively, leave M602 junct 3 and
follow signs

Imperial War Museum North features a wide
range of permanent and temporary exhibitions
exploring all the ways people's lives have been
and still are affected by war and conflict. The
award-winning building (designed by architect
Daniel Libeskind) symbolises the world torn apart
by conflict.

Times Open all year, Mar-Oct, daily 10-6; Nov-Feb
10-5. Closed 24-26 Dec. Facilities ℗ Ⓟ ⌷ ⊓
(indoor) ♿ toilets for disabled shop ⊗

MANCHESTER

The John Rylands Library

150 Deansgate M3 3EH
☎ 0161 306 0555
e-mail: jrl.visitors@manchester.ac.uk
web: www.manchester.ac.uk/library
dir: off A56, at southern end of Deansgate

Founded as a memorial to Manchester cotton-
magnate and millionaire John Rylands, this is a
public library, and also the Special Collections
Division. It is widely regarded as one of the most
beautiful libraries in the world. It extends to four
million books, manuscripts and archival items
representing some fifty cultures and ranging in
date from the third millennium BC to the present
day. Changing exhibitions throughout the year.

Times Open all year Mon, Fri & Sat 10-5, Tue &
Sun 12-5. Closed 25 Dec-1 Jan.* Facilities ℗
⌷ ♿ toilets for disabled shop ⊗

MANCHESTER

Manchester Museum

The University of Manchester, Oxford Rd
M13 9PL
☎ 0161 275 2634 & 2643
🖷 0161 275 2676
e-mail: museum@manchester.ac.uk
web: www.manchester.ac.uk/museum
dir: S of city centre on B5117

Discover the natural wonders of the world and the many cultures it is home to. The objects in the Museum's 15 galleries tell the story of the past, present and future of our planet. Come face to face with live poison dart frogs, fossils of prehistoric creatures and much more besides. Handle objects from the collection, take part in hands-on activities or enjoy a glass of wine or cup of coffee whilst exploring the latest ideas in science, culture and the arts. See website for details of family and adult events.

Times Open all year, Tue-Sat 10-5, Sun-Mon & BHs 11-4. Closed Good Fri.* Facilities ❷ ℗ ☐ ⑪ licensed ☎ (indoor) toilets for disabled shop ⊗

MANCHESTER

Museum of Science and Industry

Liverpool Rd, Castlefield M3 4FP
☎ 0161 832 2244 🖷 0161 833 1471
e-mail: marketing@mosi.org.uk
web: www.mosi.org.uk
dir: follow brown tourist signs from city centre

Uncover Manchester's industrial past and learn the fascinating stories of the people who contributed to the history and science of a city which helped shape the modern world. Located on the site of the world's oldest passenger railway station, MoSI's action-packed galleries, working exhibits and costumed characters tell the amazing story of revolutionary discoveries and remarkable inventions both past and present. There is a programme of changing exhibitions, please see the website for details.

Times Open all year, daily 10-5. Last admission 4.30. Closed 24-26 Dec & 1 Jan.* Facilities ❷ ℗ ☐ ⑪ licensed ☎ (indoor & outdoor) ♿ toilets for disabled shop ⊗

MANCHESTER

People's History Museum

Left Bank, Spinningfields M3 3ER
☎ 0161 228 7212
e-mail: info@phm.org.uk
web: www.phm.org.uk
dir: City centre, corner of Left Bank and Bridge St

The People's History Museum re-opens in late 2009 after a two-year closure and multi-million pound redevelopment. The Pump House, a former hydraulic power pumping station is being renovated to its former glory, and a new four-storey extension is being built next to it. The old and new buildings will be joined by a spectacular walkway. The Museum details the history of the British labour movement, trades unions, and other workers' organisations.

Times Open all year, Tue-Sun 10-5. Facilities ℗ ⏛ ⏢ (indoor) ♿ toilets for disabled shop ⊗

MANCHESTER

Urbis

Cathedral Gardens M4 3BG
☎ 0161 605 8200 🖷 0161 605 8201
e-mail: info@urbis.org.uk
web: www.urbis.org.uk
dir: opposite Victoria railway station

Urbis is an exhibition centre about city life. On your visit explore five floors of changing exhibitions, offering a unique insight into the culture of the modern city. Family workshops take place every weekend, see the website for details.

Times Open all year, daily 10-6.* Facilities ℗ ⏛ 🍽 licensed ⏢ (outdoor) ♿ toilets for disabled shop ⊗

MANCHESTER

The Whitworth Art Gallery

The University of Manchester, Oxford Rd
M15 6ER
☎ 0161 275 7450 📄 0161 275 7451
e-mail: whitworth@manchester.ac.uk
web: www.manchester.ac.uk/whitworth
dir: follow brown tourist signs, on Oxford Rd
(B5117) to S of city centre. Gallery in Whitworth
Park, opp Manchester Royal Infirmary

The gallery houses an impressive range of
modern and historic drawings, prints, paintings
and sculpture, as well as the largest collection
of textiles and wallpapers outside London, and
an internationally famous collection of British
watercolours. The gallery hosts an innovative
programme of touring exhibitions. A selection
of tour lectures, workshops and concerts
complement the exhibition programme.

Times Open all year, Mon-Sat 10-5, Sun 12-4.
Closed Good Fri & Xmas-New Year.* Facilities 🅿
🅟 ☐🛱 (outdoor) ♿ toilets for disabled shop
⊗

PRESTWICH

Heaton Park

Heaton Park M25 2SW
☎ 0161 773 1085 📄 0161 798 0107
e-mail: heatonpark@manchester.gov.uk
web: www.heatonpark.org.uk
dir: 4m N of Manchester city centre. M60
junct 19, S on A576, then onto A6044 & A665,
into St Margaret's Road. Park 100yds on right

600 acres of rolling parkland on the edge of
Manchester; a traditional park for the whole
family. Facilities include a Tram Museum, sports
pitches, stables, farm and animals centres, and
a horticultural centre. The hall was designed by
James Wyatt for Sir Thomas Egerton in 1772, the
house has magnificent period interiors decorated
with fine plasterwork, paintings and furniture.
Other attractions include a unique circular room
with Pompeian-style paintings, and the original
Samuel Green organ still in working order.

Times Park: Open all year, daily 8-dusk; Hall:
Open Etr-early Sep, Thu-Sun & BH 11-5.30*
Facilities 🅿 🅟 ☐🛱 (outdoor) ♿ (partly
accessible) (top floor not accessible) toilets for
disabled shop ⊗

SALFORD

The Lowry

Pier Eight, Salford Quays M50 3AZ
☎ 0870 787 5774   📠 0161 876 2001
e-mail: info@thelowry.com
web: www.thelowry.com
dir: M60 junct 12 for M602. Salford Quays is
0.25m from junct 3 of M602, follow brown Lowry
signs

The Lowry is an award-winning building housing
galleries, shops, cafés and a restaurant, plus
three theatres showing everything from West End
plays and musicals, comedians, ballet and live
bands. With regular family activity too, you can
make a whole day of your visit.

Times Open all year, daily from 10. Galleries,
Sun-Fri from 11, Sat from 10. Closed 25 Dec.*
Facilities 🅿 🅟 🖵 🍽 licensed ♿ toilets for
disabled shop ⊗

STALYBRIDGE

Astley Cheetham Art Gallery

Trinity St GK15 2BN
☎ 0161 338 6767
e-mail: astley.cheetham@tameside.gov.uk
web: www.tameside.gov.uk
dir: N of town centre

Built as a gift to the town in 1901 by mill
owner John Frederick Cheetham, this one-time
lecture hall has been an art gallery since 1932
when Cheetham left his collection to the town.
Among the works are Italian paintings from the
Renaissance, British masters such as Cox and
Burne-Jones, and more recent gifts such as
works by Turner and local artist Harry Rutherford.
The gallery hosts a programme of temporary
exhibitions of the collection and regional artists,
and a variety of workshops are run for families
throughout the year.

Times Open all year, Mon-Wed & Fri 10-12.30,
1-5; Sat 9-12.30, 1-4.* Facilities 🅟 ⊗

STOCKPORT

Hat Works Museum

Wellington Mill, Wellington Road South
SK3 0EU
☎ 0161 355 7770   📠 0161 480 8735
e-mail: bookings.hatworks@stockport.gov.uk
web: www.hatworks.org.uk
dir: M60 junct 1, on A6, Stockport town centre,
follow signs for town centre. Museum opp bus
station

Hat Works is the UK's only museum of the hatting
industry, hats and headwear, offering an insight
into a once flourishing industry. See how hats
are made with a unique working collection
of Victorian millinery machinery and take a
tour with expert guides who will give visitors
an insight into the Hatter's World. Browse an
extensive collection of hats before relaxing in the
Level 2 café. Exhibitions and events throughout
the year, contact for details. April 2010 is the
10th anniversary of the museum.

Times Open all year, Tue-Fri 10-5, Sat, Sun &
BHs 11-5. (Telephone for Xmas opening times)*
Fees Free. (Guided tours £2.60 per person)*
Facilities ℗ 💻 ♿ toilets for disabled shop ⊗

BISHOP'S WALTHAM

Bishop's Waltham Palace

SO32 1DH
☎ 01489 892460
web: www.english-heritage.org.uk
dir: on A333

Discover the medieval seat of the Bishops of
Winchester. Enjoy the wonderful moated grounds
and an exhibition about the powerful Winchester
Bishops.

Times Grounds only: May-Sep, Sun-Fri 10-5.
Farmhouse open by request.* Facilities ℗ 🍴
shop ⊗ ⛩

NETLEY

Netley Abbey

SO31 5FB

☎ 023 9258 1059

web: www.english-heritage.org.uk

dir: 4m SE of Southampton, facing Southampton Water

A romantic ruin, set among green lawns and trees, this 13th-century Cistercian abbey was founded by Peter des Roches, tutor to Henry III. Nearby is the 19th-century Gothic Netley Castle.

Times Open all year, 21 Mar-Sep, daily 10-6 (guided tour 11am Sat during Aug only); Oct-Mar, Sat-Sun 10-3. Closed 24-26 Dec & 1 Jan.* Facilities ❷ ⊗ ⌗

PORTSMOUTH

City Museum & Records Office

Museum Rd PO1 2LJ

☎ 023 9282 7261   🖷 023 9287 5276

e-mail: mvs@portsmouthcc.gov.uk

web: www.portsmouthcitymuseums.co.uk/

dir: M27/M275 into Portsmouth, follow museum symbol, City Museum on Brown signposts

Dedicated to local history, fine and decorative art, 'The Story of Portsmouth' displays room settings showing life here from the 17th century to the 1950s. The 'Portsmouth at Play' exhibition features leisure pursuits from the Victorian period to the 1970s. The museum has a fine and decorative art gallery, plus a temporary exhibition gallery with regular changing exhibitions. The Record Office contains the official records of the City of Portsmouth from the 14th century.

Times Open all year, Apr-Sep, daily 10-5.30; Oct-Mar, 10-5. Closed 24-26 Dec & Record Office closed on public hols.* Facilities ❷ Ⓟ ⬚ ⧎ (outdoor) ♿ toilets for disabled shop ⊗

PORTSMOUTH

Eastney Beam Engine House

Henderson Rd, Eastney PO4 9JF
☎ 023 9282 7261 📄 023 9287 5276
e-mail: mvs@portsmouthcc.gov.uk
web: www.portsmouthmuseums.co.uk
dir: accessible from A3(M), A27 & A2030 into
Southsea, turn left at Bransbury Park traffic
lights towards the seafront or follow signposts

The main attraction here is a magnificent pair of
James Watt Beam Engines still housed in their
original High Victorian engine house opened in
1887. One of these engines is in steam when
the museum is open. A variety of other pumping
engines, many in running order, are also on
display.

Times Open last wknd of month, 1-5 (last
admission 30 minutes before closing). Closed
Dec.* Facilities ℗ shop ⊗

PORTSMOUTH

Natural History Museum & Butterfly House

Cumberland House, Eastern Pde PO4 9RF
☎ 023 9282 7261 📄 023 9282 5276
e-mail: mvs@portsmouthcc.gov.uk
web: www.portsmouthnaturalhistory.co.uk
dir: accessed via A3(M), A27 or A2030, follow
signs to seafront

Focusing on the natural history and geology
of the area, with wildlife dioramas including
a riverbank scene with fresh water aquarium.
During the summer British and European
butterflies fly free in the Butterfly House.

Times Open all year daily, Apr-Oct 10-5.30; Nov-
Mar 10-5.* Facilities ℗ shop ⊗

SOUTHAMPTON

Southampton City Art Gallery

Civic Centre, Commercial Rd SO14 7LP
☎ 023 8083 2277 📄 023 8083 2153
e-mail: art.gallery@southampton.gov.uk
web: www.southampton.gov.uk/art
dir: situated on the Watts Park side of the
Civic Centre, a short walk from the station, on
Commercial Rd

The largest gallery in the south of England, with
the finest collection of British contemporary art
in the country outside London. Varied displays of
landscapes, portrait paintings or recent British
art are always available, as well as a special
display, selected by students.

Times Open all year, Tue-Sat 10-5, Sun 1-4.
Closed 25-26 & 31 Dec.* Facilities ℗ ⊊ ⋔◎⊺
licensed ♿ toilets for disabled shop ⊗

SOUTHAMPTON

Southampton Maritime Museum

The Wool House, Town Quay SO14 2AR
☎ 023 8022 3941 & 8063 5904
📄 023 8033 9601
e-mail: museums@southampton.gov.uk
web: www.southampton.gov.uk/leisure
dir: on the waterfront, near to the Town Quay

The Wool House was built in the 14th century
as a warehouse for wool, and now houses a
maritime museum, with models and displays
telling the history of the Victorian and modern
port of Southampton. There are exhibitions on the
Titanic, The Queen Mary and an interactive area
for children.

Times Open all year, Tue-Fri 10-4; Sat 10-1 &
2-4; Sun 1-4* Facilities ℗ shop ⊗

WINCHESTER

The Great Hall

Castle Av SO23 8PJ

☎ 01962 846476   📠 01962 841326

e-mail: the.great.hall@hants.gov.uk

web: www.hants.gov.uk/greathall

dir: at top of High St. Park & Ride recommended

The only surviving part of Winchester Castle, once home to the Domesday Book, this 13th-century hall was the centre of court and government life. Built between 1222-1235, during the reign of Henry III, it is one of the largest and finest five bay halls in England to have survived to the present day. The Round Table based on the Arthurian Legend and built between 1230-1280 hangs in the hall. Queen Eleanor's Garden is a re-creation of a late 13th century ornamental garden.

Times Open all year, Mar-Oct, daily 10-5; Nov-Feb, daily 10-4. Closed 25-26 Dec.* Facilities ⓟ ♿ toilets for disabled shop ⊗

WINCHESTER

Horse Power, The King's Royal Hussars Regimental Museum

Peninsula Barracks, Romsey Rd SO23 8TS

☎ 01962 828539 & 828541

📠 01962 828538

e-mail: curator@horsepowermuseum.co.uk

web: www.krh.org.uk

dir: M3 junct 9/10 follow city centre signs, then hospital A&E red signs to Romsey Rd. Vehicle access from Romsey Rd

Horse Power, the museum of the King's Royal Hussars, tells the exciting story of an English cavalry regiment, mounted on horses and in tanks or armoured cars.

Times Open 6 Jan-18 Dec, Tue-Fri 10-4, wknds & BHs, 12-4. (Closed daily between 12.45-1.15)* Facilities ⓟ ⓟ ⊡ ♿ toilets for disabled shop ⊗

WINCHESTER

Royal Hampshire Regiment Museum & Memorial Garden

Serle's House, Southgate St SO23 9EG

☎ 01962 863658

e-mail: museum&serleshouse.co.uk

web: www.royalhampshireregimentmuseum.co.uk

dir: near city centre. 150mtrs from lights in High St

Regimental Museum of the Royal Hampshire Regiment 1702-1992, housed in 18th-century Serles house, surrounded by the regiment's Memorial Garden. The museum tells the history of the regiment, its regulars, militia, volunteers and Territorials.

Times Normally open all year (ex 2 wks Xmas & New Year), Mon-Fri 10-4; Apr-Oct wknds & BH 12-4.* Facilities ℗ ♿ shop ⊗

HEREFORD

Old House

High Town HR1 2AA

☎ 01432 260694　📄 01432 342492

e-mail: herefordmuseums@herefordshire.gov.uk

web: www.herefordshire.gov.uk

dir: in centre of High Town

The Old House is a fine Jacobean building dating from around 1621, and was once in a row of similar houses. Its rooms are furnished in 17th-century style and give visitors the chance to learn what life was like in Cromwell's time.

Times Open all year, Tue-Sat 10-5; Apr-Sep Sun & BH Mon 10-4.* Facilities ℗ ♿ (partly accessible) (ground floor accessible) shop ⊗

BERKHAMSTED

Berkhamsted Castle

HP4 1HF
web: www.english-heritage.org.uk
dir: by Berkhamsted station

Roads and a railway have cut into the castle site, but its huge banks and ditches remain impressive. The original motte-and-bailey was built after the Norman Conquest, and there is a later stone keep, once owned by the Black Prince, eldest son of King Edward III, where King John of France was imprisoned.

Times Open all year, daily, summer 10-6; winter 10-4. Closed 25 Dec & 1 Jan.* Facilities ⚏

LETCHWORTH

Museum & Art Gallery

Broadway SG6 3PF
☎ 01462 685647   📄 01462 481879
e-mail: letchworth.museum@north-herts.gov.uk
web: www.north-herts.gov.uk
dir: next door to Public Library in town centre, near Broadway Cinema

Opened in 1914 to house the collections of the Letchworth Naturalists' Society, this friendly town-centre museum has exhibits on local wildlife, geology, arts and crafts, and archaeology. There is also a museum shop and a regular programme of art exhibitions and workshops.

Times Open all year Mon-Tue & Thu-Sat (closed BHs), 10-5. Facilities ℗ ♿ (partly accessible) (ground floor only accessible) shop ⊗

ST ALBANS

Museum of St Albans

9A Hatfield Rd AL1 3RR
☎ 01727 819340   🖷 01727 837472
e-mail: history@stalbans.gov.uk
web: www.stalbansmuseums.org.uk
dir: city centre on A1057 Hatfield road

The story of St Albans is traced from the departure of the Romans up to the present day. A variety of exhibitions are held throughout the year. The Museum is also the home of the Salaman Collection of trade and craft tools. Outside is a wildlife garden suitable for picnics.

Times Open all year, daily 10-5, Sun 2-5. Closed 25-26 Dec & 1 Jan* Facilities 🅿 🅟 ㅁ (outdoor) ♿ (partly accessible) toilets for disabled shop ⊗

TRING

The Natural History Museum at Tring

The Walter Rothschild Building, Akeman St HP23 6AP
☎ 020 7942 6171   🖷 020 7942 6150
e-mail: tring-enquiries@nhm.ac.uk
web: www.nhm.ac.uk/tring
dir: signed from A41

An unusual museum exhibiting a range of animals, collected by its founder Lionel Walter, 2nd Baron Rothschild, scientist, eccentric and natural history enthusiast. Home to the world-class research and collections of the Natural History Museum's Bird Group. A programme of temporary exhibitions, activities and events make any visit a unique day out.

Times Open all year, Mon-Sat 10-5, Sun 2-5. Closed 24-26 Dec. Facilities 🅿 🅟 ⛄ ㅁ (outdoor) toilets for disabled shop ⊗

DYMCHURCH

Dymchurch Martello Tower

High St CT16 1HU
☎ 01304 211067
web: www.english-heritage.org.uk
dir: access from High St not seafront

This artillery tower formed part of a chain of strongholds intended to resist invasion by Napoleon.

Times Open Aug BH and Heritage Open Days.*
Facilities ⊗ ♯

EDENBRIDGE

Eynsford Castle

web: www.english-heritage.org.uk
dir: in Eynsford, off A225

One of the first stone castles to be built by the Normans. The moat and remains of the curtain wall and hall can still be seen.

Times Open all year, 21 Mar-Sep, daily 10-6; Oct-Nov & Feb-Mar, daily 10-4; Dec-Jan, Wed-Sun, 10-4. Closed 24-26 Dec & 1 Jan.*
Facilities ℗ ♯

MAIDSTONE

Maidstone Museum & Bentlif Art Gallery

St Faith's St ME14 1LH
☎ 01622 602838
e-mail: museum@maidstone.gov.uk
web: www.museum.maidstone.gov.uk
dir: close to County Hall & Maidstone E train station, opposite Fremlin's Walk

Set in an Elizabethan manor house which has been much extended over the years, this museum contains an outstanding collection of fine and applied arts, including watercolours, furniture, ceramics, and a collection of Japanese art and artefacts. The museum of the Queen's Own Royal West Kent Regiment is also housed here. Please apply for details of temporary exhibitions, workshops etc.

Times Open all year, Mon-Sat 10-5.15, Sun & BH Mon 11-4. Closed 25-26 Dec & 1 Jan. Facilities ℗ ➪ & (partly accessible) shop ⊗

MAIDSTONE

Tyrwhitt Drake Museum of Carriages

The Archbishop's Stables, Mill St ME15 6YE
☎ 01622 602838
e-mail: museuminfo@maidstone.gov.uk
web: www.museum.maidstone.gov.uk
dir: close to River Medway & Archbishops Palace, just off A229 in town centre

The museum is home to a unique collection of horse-drawn vehicles and transport curiosities. More than 60 vehicles are on display, from grand carriages and ornate sleighs to antique sedan chairs and Victorian cabs, there is even an original ice-cream cart.

Times Open May-Aug, Wed-Sun & BH, 10.30-4.30.* Facilities ℗ & (partly accessible) shop ⊗

RECULVER

Reculver Towers & Roman Fort

CT6 6SU
☎ 01227 740676
web: www.english-heritage.org.uk
dir: 3m E of Herne Bay

An imposing 12th-century landmark: twin towers and the walls of a Roman fort.

Times Open any reasonable time, external viewing only.* Facilities ❷ ♯

ROCHESTER

Guildhall Museum

High St ME1 1PY
☎ 01634 848717 📄 01634 832919
e-mail: guildhall.museum@medway.gov.uk
web: www.medway.gov.uk
dir: follow signs from A2 to Rochester city centre, museum is at N end of High St

Housed in two adjacent buildings, one dating from 1687 and the other from 1909. The collections are arranged chronologically from Prehistory to the Victorian and Edwardian periods. They cover local history and archaeology, fine and decorative art. There is a gallery devoted to the prison hulks of the River Medway, and a new room detailing the links between Charles Dickens and the Medway Towns. The museum stages a regular programme of temporary exhibitions.

Times Open all year, daily (ex Mon) 10-4.30. (Last admission 4). Closed Xmas, New Year & some BHs.* Facilities ℗ ♿ (partly accessible) (limited wheelchair access to Guildhall ground floor, by prior arrangement) shop ⊗

TUNBRIDGE WELLS (ROYAL)

Tunbridge Wells Museum and Art Gallery

Civic Centre, Mount Pleasant TN1 1JN
☎ 01892 554171 & 526121
📄 01892 554131
e-mail: museum@tunbridgewells.gov.uk
web: www.tunbridgewellsmuseum.org
dir: adjacent to Town Hall, off A264

This combined museum and art gallery tells the story of the borough of Tunbridge Wells. There are collections of costume, art, dolls and toys along with natural and local history from dinosaur bones to the original Pantiles. There is also a large collection of Tunbridge ware, the intricate wooden souvenirs made for visitors to the Wells. The art gallery features a changing programme of contemporary and historic art, touring exhibitions, and local art and craft.

Times Open all year, daily 9.30-5. Sun 10-4. Closed BHs & Etr Sat. Facilities ℗ ♿ (partly accessible) (platform lift to first floor) shop ⊗

WEST MALLING

St Leonard's Tower

ME19 6PE
☎ 01732 870872
web: www.english-heritage.org.uk
dir: on unclass road W of A228

Early example of a Norman tower keep, built c.1080 by Gundulf, Bishop of Rochester. The tower stands almost to its original height and takes its name from a chapel dedicated to St Leonard that once stood nearby.

Times Open any reasonable time for exterior viewing. Internal viewing by appointment only, please call 01732 870872.* Facilities ⌗

CHORLEY

Astley Hall Museum & Art Gallery

Astley Park PR7 1NP

☎ 01257 515555 📄 01257 515923

e-mail: astley.hall@chorley.gov.uk

web: www.astleyhall.co.uk

dir: M61 junct 8, signed Botany Bay. Follow brown signs

A charming Tudor/Stuart building set in beautiful parkland, this lovely Hall retains a comfortable `lived-in' atmosphere. There are pictures and pottery to see, as well as fine furniture and rare plasterwork ceilings. Special events throughout the year.

Times Open Apr (or Etr)-Oct, Sat-Sun & BH Mon 12-5; By appointment only during the week*
Facilities 🅿 🅿 ⊼ (outdoor) shop ⊗

PRESTON

Harris Museum & Art Gallery

Market Square PR1 2PP

☎ 01772 258248 📄 01772 886764

e-mail: harris.museum@preston.gov.uk

web: www.harrismuseum.org.uk

dir: M6 junct 31, follow signs for city centre, park at bus stn car park

An impressive Grade I listed Greek Revival building containing extensive collections of fine and decorative art including a gallery of clothes and fashion. The Story of Preston covers the city's history and the lively exhibition programmes of contemporary art and social history are accompanied by events and activities throughout the year.

Times Open all year, Mon & Wed-Sat 10-5, Tue 11-5. Closed Sun & BHs.* Facilities 🅿 ⊡ ♿ (partly accessible) (lift to all floors with exception of Egyptian Balcony. Wheelchair available, chair lift to mezzanine galleries, ramp to entrance) toilets for disabled shop ⊗

PRESTON

National Football Museum

Sir Tom Finney Way, Deepdale PR1 6PA
☎ 01772 908442 📠 01772 908444
e-mail: enquiries@nationalfootballmuseum.com
web: www.nationalfootballmuseum.com
dir: 2m from M6 juncts 31, 31A or 32. Follow
brown tourist signs

Take an amazing journey through football history.
Discover the world's biggest football museum,
packed full of great footballing moments, stories
and objects -from the World Cup ball used in the
first ever final in 1930, to the ball used in the
1966 World Cup final. There are fun interactive
opportunities and the brilliant penalty shoot-out
game Goalstriker. Plus events, activities and
exhibitions all year round means there's always
something new to see and do.

Times Open all year, Tue-Sat 10-5, Sun 11-5.
Closed Mon ex BHs and school hols. (Museum
closed 15 mins before 'kick off' on match days)*
Facilities 🅿 Ⓟ ⬜ ♿ toilets for disabled shop
⊗

ROSSENDALE

Rossendale Museum

Whitaker Park, Haslingden Rd, Rawtenstall
BB4 6RE
☎ 01706 260785 📠 01706 250037
e-mail: rossendale.museum@lancashire.gov.uk
web: www.lancashire.gov.uk/museums
dir: off A681, 0.25m W of Rawtenstall centre

Former mill owner's house, built in 1840 and set
in the delightful Whitaker Park. Displays include
fine and decorative arts, a Victorian drawing
room, natural history, costume, local and social
history and regular temporary exhibitions.

Times Open all year, Apr-Oct, Tue-Thu, Sat-Sun &
BHs, 1-4.30; Nov-Mar, 1-4.* Facilities 🅿 Ⓟ ♿
toilets for disabled shop ⊗

DONINGTON-LE-HEATH

Donington-le-Heath Manor House

Manor Rd LE67 2FW
☎ 01530 831259 ▤ 01530 831259
e-mail: dlhmanorhouse@leics.gov.uk
web: www.leics.gov.uk/donington
dir: S of Coalville

This is a rare example of a medieval manor house, tracing its history back to about 1280. It has now been restored as a period house, with fine oak furnishings. The surrounding grounds include period gardens, and the adjoining stone barn houses a restaurant.

Times Open Mar-Nov, daily 11-4, Dec-Feb, Sat-Sun 11-4. Facilities ❷ ❑ ⑩ licensed ⋒ ♿ (partly accessible) toilets for disabled shop ⊗

LEICESTER

Abbey Pumping Station

Corporation Rd, Abbey Ln LE4 5PX
☎ 0116 299 5111 ▤ 0116 299 5125
e-mail: museums@leicester.gov.uk
web: www.leicester.gov.uk/museums
dir: off A6, 1m N from city centre

Explore Leicester's industrial, technological and scientific heritage at Abbey Pumping Station. Built in 1891, this fascinating museum features some of the largest steam beam engines in the country and a working model railway. Exhibitions include historic transport, light and optics, and public health. There are plenty of interactive exhibits, popular with children.

Times Open Feb-Oct, daily 11-4.30. Open Nov-Jan for special events. Fees Admission free, a small charge made for some events. Donations welcome. Facilities ❷ ⋒ (outdoor) ♿ (partly accessible) (limited wheelchair access) toilets for disabled shop ⊗

LEICESTER

The Record Office for Leicestershire & Rutland

Long St, Wigston Magna LE18 2AH
☎ 0116 257 1080 📠 0116 257 1120
e-mail: recordoffice@leics.gov.uk
web: www.leics.gov.uk/recordoffice
dir: old A50, S of Leicester City

Housed in a converted 19th-century school in Wigston, the Record Office holds photographs, electoral registers and archive film, files of local newspapers, history tapes and sound recordings, all of which can be studied.

Times Open all year, Mon, Tue & Thu 9.15-5, Wed 9.15-7.30, Fri 9.15-4.45, Sat 9.15-12.15. Closed Sun & BH wknds Sat-Tue. Facilities 🅿 🅿 ♿ toilets for disabled ⊗ 🚐

LINCOLN

Museum of Lincolnshire Life

Burton Rd LN1 3LY
☎ 01522 528448 📠 01522 521264
e-mail: lincolnshirelife.museum@lincolnshire. gov.uk
web: www.lincolnshire.gov.uk/ museumoflincolnshirelife
dir: 5 min walk from Lincoln Castle

A large and varied social history museum, where two centuries of Lincolnshire life are illustrated by enthralling displays of domestic implements, industrial machinery, agricultural tools and a collection of horse-drawn vehicles. The exciting and interactive Royal Lincolnshire Regiment Museum contains videos, an audio tour, and touch screen computers. Various events throughout the year.

Times Open all year, Apr-Sep, daily 10-4; Oct-Mar, Mon-Sat 10-4 (last admission 3.30). Closed 24-26 & 31 Dec, 1 Jan. Facilities 🅿 🅿 ⊑ ♿ toilets for disabled shop ⊗

LINCOLN

Usher Gallery

Lindum Rd LN2 1NN
☎ 01522 550990 ▤ 01522 550991
e-mail: thecollection@lincolnshire.gov.uk
web: www.thecollection.lincoln.museum
dir: follow signs for Lincoln City Centre, then
parking for cultural quarter, then pedestrian
signs to The Collection

Built as the result of a bequest by Lincoln
jeweller James Ward Usher, the Gallery houses
his magnificent collection of watches, porcelain
and miniatures, as well as topographical
works, watercolours by Peter de Wint, Tennyson
memorabilia and coins. The gallery has a popular
and changing display of contemporary visual arts
and crafts. There is a lively lecture programme
and children's activity diary.

Times Open all year, daily 10-4 ex 24-26 Dec
& 1 Jan (last entry 3.30)* Facilities ℗ ⊡ ⊞
(outdoor) ⅋ toilets for disabled shop ⊗

STAMFORD

Stamford Museum

Broad St PE9 1PJ
☎ 01780 766317 ▤ 01780 480363
e-mail: stamford_museum@lincolnshire.gov.uk
web: www.lincolnshire.gov.uk/stamfordmuseum
dir: from A1 follow town centre signs from any
Stamford exit

Displays illustrate the history of this fine stone
town and include Stamford Ware pottery, the visit
of Daniel Lambert and the Town's more recent
industrial past. The Stamford Tapestry depicts
the history of the town in wool.

Times Open all year, Mon-Sat 10-4. Closed 24-26
& 31 Dec & 1 Jan.* Facilities ℗ ⅋ shop ⊗

Geffrye Museum

136 Kingsland Rd, Shoreditch E2 8EA
☎ 020 7739 9893 🖹 020 7729 5647
e-mail: info@geffrye-museum.org.uk
web: www.geffrye-museum.org.uk
dir: S end of Kingsland Rd A10 in Shoreditch
between Cremer St & Pearson St

The only museum in the UK to specialise in the domestic interiors and furniture of the urban middle classes. Displays span the 400 years from 1600 to the present day, forming a sequence of period rooms which capture the nature of English interior style. The museum is set in elegant, 18th-century buildings, surrounded by delightful gardens including an award-winning walled herb garden and a series of historical gardens which highlight changes in town gardens from the 17th to 20th centuries. One of the museum's historic almshouses has been fully restored to its original condition and is open on selected days (ring for details). Each December, the museum's period rooms are decorated in authentic, festive style to reflect 400 years of Christmas traditions in English homes.

Times Open all year, Tue-Sat 10-5, Sun & BH Mon 12-5. Closed Mon, Good Fri, 24-26 Dec & New Year.* Facilities ℗ ⑩ licensed 🛪 (outdoor) ♿ toilets for disabled shop ⊗

V & A Museum of Childhood

Cambridge Heath Rd E2 9PA
☎ 020 8983 5200 🖹 020 8983 5225
e-mail: moc@vam.ac.uk
web: www.museumofchildhood.org.uk
dir: Underground - Bethnal Green

The V&A Museum of Childhood re-opened following an extensive transformation a few years ago. There is a stunning new entrance, fully updated galleries and displays, a brand new gallery and expanded public spaces. Galleries include Creativity, Moving Toys and Childhood Galleries. There is also a full programme of activities. Exhibitions include Sit Down, Seating for kids.

Times Open all year, daily 10-5.45. Closed 25-26 Dec & 1 Jan. Facilities ℗ ⬜ 🛪 (outdoor) ♿ toilets for disabled shop ⊗

LONDON E17

William Morris Gallery

Lloyd Park, Forest Rd, Walthamstow E17 4PP
☎ 020 8496 4390 🖷 020 8527 7070
e-mail: wmg.enquiries@walthamforest.gov.uk
web: www.walthamforest.gov.uk/william-morris
dir: Underground - Blackhorse Rd, take bus no.
123 along Forest Rd, get off at the Lloyd Park
stop or Walthamstow Central, N 15m along Hoe
St, left into Gaywood Rd to Lloyd Park

Victorian artist, craftsman, poet and free thinker
William Morris lived here from 1848 to 1856,
and the gallery houses displays illustrating his
life and work. Exhibits include fabrics, stained
glass, wallpaper and furniture, as well as Pre-
Raphaelite paintings, ceramics and a collection
of pictures by Frank Brangwyn, who worked briefly
for Morris.

Times Open all year, Wed-Sun 10-5.*
Facilities 🅿 🅿 ♿ (partly accessible) shop ⊗

LONDON EC2

Bank of England Museum

Bartholomew Ln EC2R 8AH
☎ 020 7601 5545 🖷 020 7601 5808
e-mail: museum@bankofengland.co.uk
web: www.bankofengland.co.uk/museum
dir: museum housed in Bank of London, entrance
in Bartholomew Lane. Bank underground, exit 2

The museum tells the story of the Bank of
England from its foundation in 1694 to its role in
today's economy. Interactive programmes with
graphics and video help explain its many and
varied roles. Popular exhibits include a unique
collection of banknotes and a genuine gold bar,
which may be handled.

Times Open all year, Mon-Fri 10-5. Closed wknds
& BHs. Open on day of Lord Mayor's Show &
Open House London Facilities 🅿 ♿ toilets for
disabled shop ⊗

LONDON EC2

The Guildhall

Gresham St EC2V 5AE
☎ 020 7606 3030 📄 020 7260 1119
e-mail: pro@corpoflondon.gov.uk
web: www.cityoflondon.gov.uk
dir: Underground - Bank, St Paul's

The Court of Common Council (presided over by the Lord Mayor) administers the City of London and meets in the Guildhall. Dating from 1411, the building was badly damaged in the Great Fire and again in the Blitz. The great hall, traditionally used for the Lord Mayor's Banquet and other important civic functions, is impressively decorated with the banners and shields of the livery companies, of which there are more than 90. The Clock Museum, which has a collection of 700 exhibits, charts the history of 500 years of time-keeping.

Times Open all year, May-Sep, daily 10-5; Oct-Apr, Mon-Sat 10-5. Closed Xmas, New Year, Good Fri, Etr Mon & infrequently for Civic occasions. Please contact 020 7606 3030 ext 1463 before visit to be certain of access.* Facilities ℗ toilets for disabled shop ⊗

LONDON EC2

Museum of London

150 London Wall EC2Y 5HN
☎ 0870 444 3851 📄 0870 444 3853
e-mail: info@museumoflondon.org.uk
web: www.museumoflondon.org.uk
dir: Underground - St Paul's, Barbican. N of St Paul's Cathedral at the end of St Martins le Grand and S of the Barbican. S of Aldersgate St

Dedicated to the story of London and its people, the Museum of London exists to inspire a passion for London in all who visit it. As well as the permanent collection, the Museum has a varied exhibition programme with major temporary exhibitions and topical displays each year. There are also smaller exhibitions in the foyer gallery. A wide programme of lectures and events explore London's history and its evolution into the city of today.

Times Open all year, Mon-Sat 10-5.50, Sun 12-5.50. Last admission 5.30.* Facilities ℗ ℗ ⊑ ⊓ toilets for disabled shop ⊗

LONDON EC4

Middle Temple Hall

The Temple EC4Y 9AT
☎ 020 7427 4800 & 4820
▤ 020 7427 4801
e-mail: banqueting@middletemple.org.uk
web: www.middletemple.org.uk
dir: Underground - Temple, Blackfriars. Turn left at the embankment & left into Middle Temple Lane. Hall half way up on left

Between Fleet Street and the Thames are the Middle and Inner Temples, separate Inns of Court, so named after the Knights Templar who occupied the site from about 1160. Middle Temple Hall is a fine example of Tudor architecture, completed in about 1570, and has a double hammerbeam roof and beautiful stained glass. The 29ft-long high table was made from a single oak tree from Windsor Forest. Sir Francis Drake was a visitor to and friend of the Middle Temple, and a table made from timbers from his ship, the Golden Hind, survives to this day.

Times Open all year, Mon-Fri 10-12 & 3-4. Closed BH & legal vacations.* Facilities ℗ ⬛ ⦿ licensed & toilets for disabled shop

LONDON NW3

Kenwood House

Hampstead Ln NW3 7JR
☎ 020 8348 1286 ▤ 020 7973 3891
web: www.english-heritage.org.uk
dir: Underground - Hampstead

In splendid grounds beside Hampstead Heath, this outstanding neo-classical house contains one of the most important collections of paintings ever given to the nation. Works by Rembrandt, Vermeer, Turner, Gainsborough and Reynolds are all set against a backdrop of sumptuous rooms. Scenes from Notting Hill and Mansfield Park were filmed here.

Times Open all year, Apr-Mar, daily 11.30-4. Closed 24-26 Dec & 1 Jan. (The park stays open later, please see site notices). Facilities ℗ ⬛ ⦿ licensed ⪥ toilets for disabled shop ✿

LONDON NW9

Royal Air Force Museum London

Grahame Park Way, Colindale NW9 5LL
☎ 020 8205 2266 📠 020 8358 4981
e-mail: groups@rafmuseum.org
web: www.rafmuseum.org
dir: within easy reach of the A5, A41, M1 and North Circular A406 roads. Tube on Northern Line to Colindale. Rail to Mill Hill Broadway station. Bus route 303 passes the door

Take off to the Royal Air Force Museum London and soar through the history of aviation from the earliest balloon flights to the latest Eurofighter. This is a world-class collection of over 100 aircraft, aviation/wartime memorabilia and artefacts together with an impressive sound and light show that takes you back to the Battle of Britain. The Aeronauts Interactive Centre offers hands-on entertainment and education for all ages and includes cockpit controls, co-ordination tests, engine lifting, air speed, drop zone, pilot testing and more. The museum will celebrate the 70th anniversary Battle of Britain 11th to 12th September 2010, various other events throughout the year.

Times Open all year, daily 10-6. (Last admission 5.30). Closed 24-26 Dec, 1 & 11-15 Jan.
Facilities 🅿 Ⓟ 🖵 🍽 licensed 🎪 (indoor & outdoor) ♿ toilets for disabled shop ⊗

LONDON SE1

Bankside Gallery

48 Hopton St SE1 9JH
☎ 020 7928 7521 📠 020 7928 2820
e-mail: info@banksidegallery.com
web: www.banksidegallery.com
dir: E of Blackfriars Bridge, South Bank of the Thames, adjacent to Tate Modern and the Millennium Bridge

Bankside Gallery is the home of the Royal Watercolour Society (RWS) and the Royal Society of Painter-Printmakers (RE). A series of regularly changing exhibitions throughout the year displays the work of both societies, and other prestigious contemporary artists.

Times Open all year, daily during exhibitions 11-6.* Facilities Ⓟ shop ⊗

LONDON SE1

Imperial War Museum

Lambeth Rd SE1 6HZ
☎ 020 7416 5320 & 5321
🖹 020 7416 5374
e-mail: mail@iwm.org.uk
web: www.iwm.org.uk
dir: Underground - Lambeth North, Elephant &
Castle or Waterloo

Founded in 1917, this museum illustrates
and records all aspects of the two World Wars
and other military operations involving Britain
and the Commonwealth since 1914. There are
always special exhibitions and the programme
of special and family events includes film shows
and lectures. The museum also has an extensive
film, photography, sound, document and art
archive as well as a library, although some
reference departments are open to the public
by appointment only. In 2010 it will be 70 years
since the Battle of Britain, and the introduction
of rationing.

Times Open all year, daily 10-6. Closed 24-26
Dec.* Fees Free admission (charges apply for
some temporary exhibitions)* Facilities ⓟ ⏛
🍽 licensed ⋒ (indoor & outdoor) ♿ toilets for
disabled shop ⊗

LONDON SE1

Tate Modern

Bankside SE1 9TG
☎ 020 7887 8008 (info) & 8888
🖹 020 7401 5052
e-mail: information@tate.org.uk
web: www.tate.org.uk
dir: Underground - Southwark, Blackfriars

This is the UK's largest museum of modern art
and is housed in the impressive Bankside power
station. Entrance to the permanent collection,
which includes works from artists like Picasso,
Warhol and Dalí, is free. Tate Modern also holds
world-acclaimed temporary exhibitions as well as
education programmes, events and activities.

Times Open all year, Sun-Thu 10-6 (last
admission 5.15), Fri & Sat 10am-10pm (last
admission 9.15). Closed 24-26 Dec.*
Facilities ⓟ ⏛ 🍽 licensed ♿ toilets for
disabled shop ⊗

LONDON SE5

South London Gallery

65 Peckham Rd SE5 8UH

☎ 020 7703 6120 & 9799 (info)

🖨 020 7252 4730

e-mail: mail@southlondongallery.org

web: www.southlondongallery.org

dir: from Vauxhall take A202 to Camberwell Green. Gallery halfway between Camberwell Green and Peckham

The gallery presents a programme of up to six exhibitions a year of cutting-edge contemporary art, and has established itself as South East London's premier venue for contemporary visual arts. The Gallery also programmes regular talks, screenings, live art projects and a range of activities for families and young people.

Times Open all year, Tue-Sun, 12-6. Closed Mon* Facilities ℗ ♿ (partly accessible) (not accessible for electric wheelchairs) toilets for disabled shop ⊗

LONDON SE10

National Maritime Museum

Romney Rd SE10 9NF

☎ 020 8312 6565 🖨 020 8312 6632

e-mail: RScates@nmm.ac.uk

web: www.nmm.ac.uk

dir: central Greenwich A206

Britain's seafaring history is displayed in this impressive modern museum. Themes include exploration and discovery, Nelson, trade and empire, passenger shipping and luxury liners, maritime London, costume, art and the sea, and the future of the sea. There are interactive displays for children.

Times Open all year, daily 10-5 Closed 24-26 Dec. (Partial closures 31 Dec, 1 Jan & Marathon day). Fees Free, except some special exhibtions. Facilities ℗ ⛲🍴 (outdoor) ♿ toilets for disabled shop ⊗

LONDON SE10

Old Royal Naval College

Greenwich SE10 9LW
☎ 020 8269 4747 📄 020 8269 4757
e-mail: info@greenwichfoundation.org.uk
web: www.oldroyalnavalcollege.org
dir: In centre of Greenwich, off one way system, (College Approach), on the Thames next to Greenwich Pier

The Old Royal Naval College is one of London's most famous riverside landmarks and a masterpiece of Baroque architecture. The buildings, designed by Sir Christopher Wren as the Greenwich Hospital, occupy the site of the palace where Henry VIII and Elizabeth I were born, and incorporate the Painted Hall by James Thornhill and the Chapel by James Stuart. The public can visit the grounds and also Discover Greenwich, a major new historical education and interpretation centre.

Times Open all year ex 24-26 Dec. (Painted Hall & Chapel), daily 10-5. Chapel open to visitors from 12.30 on Sun, public worship from 11.* Fees Admission free, guided tours £5 (ch under 16 free). Group tours of more than 10 people booking necessary.* Facilities ℗ 🍴 licensed ㅠ (outdoor) ♿ (partly accessible) (several stairs make access difficult, stairmate available for Painted Hall & Chapel) toilets for disabled ⊗

LONDON SE10

The Queens House

Romney Rd, Greenwich SE10 9NF
☎ 020 8312 6565 📄 020 8312 6632
e-mail: bookings@nmm.ac.uk
web: www.nmm.ac.uk
dir: central Greenwich A206

The first Palladian-style villa in England, designed by Inigo Jones for Anne of Denmark and completed for Queen Henrietta Maria, wife of Charles I. The Great Hall, the State Rooms and a Loggia overlooking Greenwich Park are notable features. Also displays the extensive art collection of the National Maritime Museum including Tudor and Stuart royalty.

Times Open all year, daily 10-5. Closed 24-26 Dec. (Partial closures 31 Dec, 1 Jan & Marathon day). Fees Free, except some special exhibitions Facilities ℗ 旦ㅠ (outdoor) ♿ toilets for disabled shop ⊗

LONDON SE23

The Horniman Museum & Gardens

London Rd, Forest Hill SE23 3PQ
☎ 020 8699 1872 📄 020 8291 5506
e-mail: enquiry@horniman.ac.uk
web: www.horniman.ac.uk
dir: situated on A205

Founder Frederick Horniman, a tea merchant, gave the museum to the people of London in 1901. The collection covers the natural and cultural world including Natural History with displays on Vanishing Birds and African Worlds, The Music Gallery, which displays Britain's largest collection of musical instruments and the Centenary Gallery which showcases world cultures. There are 16 acres of gardens, and the museum hosts a variety of workshops and activities for all ages.

Times Open all year, daily 10.30-5.30. Closed 24-26 Dec. Gardens close at sunset.* Facilities ℗ ☕🍴 (outdoor) toilets for disabled shop ⊗

LONDON SW1

Tate Britain

Millbank SW1P 4RG
☎ 020 7887 8888 & rec info 8008
e-mail: information@tate.org.uk
web: www.tate.org.uk
dir: Underground - Pimlico

Tate Britain is the national gallery of British art from 1500 to the present day, from Tudors to the Turner Prize. Tate holds the greatest collection of British art in the world, including works by Blake, Constable, Epstein, Gainsborough, Gilbert and George, Hatoum, Hirst, Hockney, Hodgkin, Hogarth, Moore, Rossetti, Sickert, Spencer, Stubbs and Turner. The gallery is the world centre for the understanding and enjoyment of British art.

Times Open all year, daily 10-5.50. Closed 24-26 Dec.* Facilities ℗ ☕🍴 licensed ☂ (indoor & outdoor) ♿ toilets for disabled shop ⊗

LONDON SW1

Westminster Cathedral

Victoria St SW1P 1QW
☎ 020 7798 9055   📠 020 7798 9090
e-mail: barrypalmer@rcdow.org.uk
web: www.westminstercathedral.org.uk
dir: 300 yds from Victoria Station

Westminster Cathedral is a fascinating example of Victorian architecture. Designed in the Early Christian Byzantine style by John Francis Bentley, its strongly oriental appearance makes it very distinctive. The foundation stone was laid in 1895 but the interior decorations are not fully completed. The Campanile Bell Tower is 273ft high and has a four-sided viewing gallery with magnificent views over London. The lift is open daily 9am-5pm Mar-Nov but shut Mon-Wed from Dec-Feb.

Times Open all year, daily 7am-7pm.*
Facilities ℗ ⛽ shop 🚫

LONDON SW3

National Army Museum

Royal Hospital Rd, Chelsea SW3 4HT
☎ 020 7730 0717   📠 020 7823 6573
e-mail: info@national-army-museum.ac.uk
web: www.national-army-museum.ac.uk
dir: Underground - Sloane Square

The museum will guide you through Britain's Military History and its effect on Britain and the world today. Permanent gallery displays, exhibitions, celebrity speakers, lectures and special events will both engage and entertain you.

Times Open all year, daily 10-5.30. Closed Good Fri, May Day, 24-26 Dec & 1 Jan.* Facilities ℗ ℗ ⛽♿ toilets for disabled shop 🚫

LONDON SW3

Royal Hospital Chelsea

Royal Hospital Rd SW3 4SR

☎ 020 7881 5200   📄 020 7881 5463

e-mail: info@chelsea-pensioners.org.uk

web: www.chelsea-pensioners.org.uk

dir: near Sloane Square, off A3216 & A3031

Founded in 1682 by Charles II as a retreat for army veterans who had become unfit for duty, through injury or long service, the Royal Hospital Chelsea was built on the site of a theological college founded by James I in 1610. The buildings were designed and built by Sir Christopher Wren, and then added to by Robert Adam and Sir John Soane. The hospital houses some 300 'In-Pensioners', some of whom do voluntary work as tour guides, clerical assistants and ground staff. Visitors can stroll around the grounds, gain admission to the Chapel, Great Hall and visit the Museum.

Times Open all year, daily Mon-Sat, 10-12 & 2-4, Sun 2-4. (Museum closed on Sun Oct-Mar). Closed 25-26 Dec & Good Friday.* Facilities ℗ ㅠ (outdoor) ♿ (partly accessible) toilets for disabled shop ⊗

LONDON SW7

The Natural History Museum

Cromwell Rd SW7 5BD

☎ 020 7942 5000   📄 020 7942 5075

e-mail: feedback@nhm.ac.uk

web: www.nhm.ac.uk

dir: Underground - South Kensington

This vast and elaborate Romanesque-style building, with its terracotta tiles showing relief mouldings of animals, birds and fishes, covers an area of four acres. Holding over 70 million specimens from all over the globe, from dinosaurs to diamonds and earthquakes to ants, the museum provides a journey into Earth's past, present and future. Discover more about the work of the museum through a daily programme of talks from museum scientists or go behind the scenes of the Darwin Centre, the museum's scientific research centre.

Times Open all year, daily 10-5.50 (last admission 5.30). Closed 24-26 Dec. Fees Free. Charge made for some special exhibitions. Facilities ℗ ⊑ ⑩ licensed ㅠ (indoor) ♿ (partly accessible) (top floor/one gallery not accessible) toilets for disabled shop ⊗

LONDON SW7

Science Museum

Exhibition Rd, South Kensington SW7 2DD
☎ 0870 870 4868 📠 020 7942 4421
e-mail: sciencemuseum@sciencemuseum.org.uk
web: www.sciencemuseum.org.uk
dir: Underground - South Kensington, signed
from tube stn

See iconic objects from the history of science,
from Stephenson's Rocket to the Apollo 10
command module; be amazed by a 3D IMAX
movie; take a ride in a simulator; visit an
exhibition; and encounter the past, present
and future of technology in seven floors of free
galleries, including the famous hands-on section
where children can have fun investigating
science with the Museum's dedicated Explainers.
The Museum is free, but charges apply to the
IMAX cinema, special exhibitions and simulators.

Times Open all year, daily 10-6. Closed 24-26
Dec. Fees Admission free. Charges apply for
IMAX 3D cinema, simulators & some special
exhibitions. Facilities ℗ ☐ 🍽 licensed 🎏
(indoor) ♿ toilets for disabled shop ⊗

LONDON SW7

Victoria and Albert Museum

Cromwell Rd, South Kensington SW7 2RL
☎ 020 7942 2000
e-mail: vanda@vam.ac.uk
web: www.vam.ac.uk
dir: Underground - South Kensington, Museum
situated on A4, Buses C1, 14, 74, 414 stop
outside the Cromwell Road entrance

The V&A is the world's greatest museum of
art and design. It was established in 1852
to make important works of art available to
all, and also to inspire British designers and
manufacturers. The Museum's rich and diverse
collections span over three thousand years of
human creativity from many parts of the world,
and include ceramics, furniture, fashion, glass,
jewellery, metalwork, sculpture, textiles and
paintings. Highlights include the British Galleries
1500-1900, the Jameel Gallery of Islamic Art, and
the magnificent John Madejski Garden.

Times Open all year, daily 10-5.45. Fri 10am-
10pm* Facilities ℗ ☐ 🍽 licensed 🎏
(outdoor) toilets for disabled shop ⊗

LONDON W1

The Wallace Collection

Hertford House, Manchester Square W1U 3BN
☎ 020 7563 9500 📠 020 7224 2155
e-mail: visiting@wallacecollection.org
web: www.wallacecollection.org
dir: Underground - Bond St, Baker St, Oxford Circus, located minutes from Oxford St, in garden square behind Selfridges

Founded by the 1st Marquis of Hertford, the Wallace Collection was bequeathed to the nation in 1897 and came on public display three years later. This is one of the world's finest collections of art ever assembled by one family. The collection is shown in the family home, a tranquil oasis just a few minutes from Oxford Street. There are paintings by Titian, Canaletto, Rembrandt, Rubens, Hals, Fragonard, Velazquez, Gainsborough and many more. There is a very important collection of French porcelain and furniture, much of it of Royal providence, as well as amazing arms and armour, sculpture and Renaissance treasures. Many rooms have been recently restored creating wonderful intimate and opulent settings for the works of art.

Times Open all year, daily 10-5, closed 24-26 Dec & 1 Jan.* Facilities ⓟ 🖵🍴 licensed ♿ toilets for disabled shop ⊗

LONDON W2

Serpentine Gallery

Kensington Gardens W2 3XA
☎ 020 7402 6075 📠 020 7402 4103
e-mail: press@serpentinegallery.org
web: www.serpentinegallery.org
dir: Underground - Knightsbridge, Lancaster Gate, South Kensington. Bus 9, 10, 12, 52, 94

The Serpentine Gallery, named after the lake in Hyde Park, is situated in the heart of Kensington Gardens in a 1934 tea pavilion, and was founded in 1970 by the Arts Council of Great Britain. Today the Gallery attracts over 400,000 visitors a year and is one the best places in London for modern and contemporary art and architecture.

Times Open all year, daily 10-6.* Facilities ♿ toilets for disabled shop ⊗

LONDON W4

Hogarth's House

Hogarth Ln, Great West Rd W4 2QN
☎ 020 8994 6757 📄 0845 456 2880
e-mail: info@cip.org.uk
web: www.hounslow.info
dir: 50yds W of Hogarth rdbt on Great West Road A4

This 18th-century house was the country home of artist William Hogarth (1697-1764) during the last 15 years of his life. The house contains displays on the artist's life, and many of his satirical engravings. The gardens contain Hogarth's famous mulberry tree.

Times Open all year, Apr-Oct, Tue-Fri 1-5, Sat-Sun 1-6; Nov-Mar, Tue-Fri 1-4, Sat-Sun 1-5. Closed Mon (ex BHs), Jan, Good Fri & 25-26 Dec.* Facilities ℗ toilets for disabled shop ⊗

LONDON WC1

British Museum

Great Russell St WC1B 3DG
☎ 020 7323 8000 📄 020 7323 8616
e-mail: information@britishmuseum.org
web: www.thebritishmuseum.ac.uk
dir: Underground - Russell Sq, Tottenham Court Rd, Holborn

Of the world and for the world, the British Museum brings together astounding examples of universal heritage, for free. Enter through the largest covered square in Europe. Pick up your audio guide, children's pack or What's On programme. Then discover the world through objects like the Aztec mosaics, the Rosetta Stone, El Anatsui's African textiles or the colossal Ramesses II. And if you want a more intimate look, a fantastic evening meal or some world cinema, come late - every Thursday and Friday.

Times Open all year, Gallery: 10-5.30 selected galleries open late Thu-Fri until 8.30. Great Court: Sun-Wed 9-6, Thu-Sat 9am-11pm. Closed Good Fri, 24-26 Dec & 1 Jan.* Facilities ℗ ☕ 🍽 licensed ㅠ (indoor) toilets for disabled shop ⊗

Petrie Museum of Egyptian Archaeology

Malet Place, Univerity College London
WC1E 6BT
☎ 020 7679 2884 📄 020 7679 2886
e-mail: petrie.museum@ucl.ac.uk
web: www.petrie.ucl.ac.uk
dir: on 1st floor of the D M S Watson building, in Malet Place, off Torrington Place, UCL Main Campus

One of the largest and most inspiring collections of Egyptian archaeology anywhere in the world. The displays illustrate life in the Nile Valley from prehistory, through the era of the Pharoahs to Roman and Islamic times. Especially noted for its collection of the personal items that illustrate life and death in Ancient Egypt, including the world's earliest surviving dress (c 2800BC).

Times Open all year, Tue-Sat 1-5. Closed for 1 wk at Xmas & Etr. Facilities ♿ (partly accessible) (objects on rear staircase which make it inaccessible to wheelchairs) toilets for disabled shop ⊗

Hunterian Museum

The Royal College of Surgeons, 35-43 Lincoln's Inn Fields WC2A 3PE
☎ 020 7869 6560 📄 020 7869 6564
e-mail: museums@rcseng.ac.uk
web: www.rcseng.ac.uk
dir: Underground - Holborn

The Hunterian Museum at the Royal College of Surgeons houses over 3000 anatomical and pathological preparations collected by the surgeon John Hunter (1728-1793). New interpretive displays explore Hunter's life and work, the history of the Hunterian Museum and the College, and the development of surgery from the 18th century to the present. The MacRae Gallery provides a dedicated space for learning based on the museum's reserve collections. The museum also stages a changing programme of temporary exhibitions, lectures and other public events on themes related to the history and current practice of surgery.

Times Open all year Tue-Sat 10-5. Facilities ℗ ♿ toilets for disabled shop ⊗

LONDON WC2

National Gallery

Trafalgar Square WC2N 5DN
☎ 020 7747 2885 ⓑ 020 7747 2423
e-mail: information@ng-london.org.uk
web: www.nationalgallery.org.uk
dir: Underground - Charing Cross, Leicester
Square, Embankment & Piccadilly Circus. Rail -
Charing Cross. Located on N side of Trafalgar Sq

All the great periods of Western European
painting from the Middle Ages to the early 20th
century are represented here. Artists on display
include Leonardo da Vinci, Rembrandt, Titian,
Caravaggio, Turner, Monet and Van Gogh. Major
exhibitions and events throughout the year.

Times Open all year, daily 10-6, (Fri until
9). Special major changing exhibitions open
normal gallery times. Closed 24-26 Dec & 1 Jan.
Fees Free. Admission charged for some major
exhibitions. Facilities ⓟ ⌨ ⍾ licensed ♿
toilets for disabled shop ⊗

LONDON WC2

National Portrait Gallery

St Martin's Place WC2H 0HE
☎ 020 7306 0055 ⓑ 020 7306 0056
web: www.npg.org.uk
dir: Underground - Charing Cross, Leicester
Square. Buses to Trafalgar Square

The National Portrait Gallery is home to the
largest collection of portraiture in the world
featuring famous British men and woman who
have created history from the Middle Ages until
the present day. Over 1000 portraits are on
display across three floors from Henry VIII and
Florence Nightingale to The Beatles and HM The
Queen. If you want to rest your weary feet, visit
the fabulous Portrait Restaurant on the top floor
with roof-top views across London. Special events
take place throughout the year, see website for
details.

Times Open all year, Mon-Wed & Sat-Sun 10-6,
Thu-Fri 10-9. Closed Good Fri, 24-26 Dec & 1
Jan. (Gallery closure commences 10mins prior to
stated time).* Fees Free ex special exhibitions
Facilities ⓟ ⌨ ⍾ licensed ♿ toilets for
disabled shop ⊗

Sir John Soane's Museum

13 Lincoln's Inn Fields WC2A 3BP
☎ 020 7405 2107 📄 020 7831 3957
e-mail: sbhatti@soane.org.uk
web: www.soane.org
dir: Underground - Holborn

Sir John Soane was responsible for some of the most splendid architecture in London, and his house, built in 1812, contains his collections of antiquities, sculpture, paintings, drawings and books. Amongst his treasures are the Rake's Progess, the Election series of paintings by Hogarth and the Sarcophagus of Seti I.

Times Open all year, Tue-Sat 10-5. Also first Tue of month 6-9pm. (Closed BH, Good Fri & 24 Dec). Lecture tour Sat 11am (limited no of tickets sold from 10.30). Fees Free entry, donations welcome. Facilities ℗ ♿ (partly accessible) (phone 020 7440 4263 for details) shop ⊗

Theatre Museum

Victoria and Albert Museum, Cromwell Rd
SW7 2RL
☎ 020 7943 4700 📄 020 7943 4777
e-mail: tmenquiries@vam.ac.uk
web: www.vam.ac.uk/theatre
dir: Underground - Covent Garden, Leicester Sq

The Theatre Museum has moved and is now housed in the Victoria and Albert Museum. New Performance galleries celebrate the performing arts in Britain, from Shakespeare to the present day.

Times Open all year, daily 10-6. Closed 24-26 Dec & 1 Jan.* Facilities ℗ ℗ ⊡ ⊙ licensed ♿ toilets for disabled shop ⊗

BARNET

Museum of Domestic Design & Architecture

Middlesex University, Cat Hill EN4 8HT
☎ 020 8411 5244   📠 020 8411 6639
e-mail: moda@mdx.ac.uk
web: www.moda.mdx.ac.uk
dir: from M25, junct 24 signed A111 Cockfosters to Cat Hill rdbt, straight over onto Chase side. Entrance 1st right opposite Chicken Shed Theatre on Cat Hill Campus

MoDA is a museum of the history of the home. It holds one of the world's most comprehensive collections of decorative design for the period 1870 to 1960, and is a rich source of information on how people decorated and lived in their homes. MoDA has two galleries, a lecture theatre for study days, a seminar room with practical workshops for both adults and children, and a study room which gives visitors access to the collections.

Times Open all year, Tue-Sat 10-5, Sun 2-5. Closed Mon, Etr, Xmas & New Year. Fees Free entrance. Charges for study days, workshop & group tours Facilities ❷ ♿ toilets for disabled shop ⊗

KEW

The National Archives

Ruskin Av TW9 4DU
☎ 020 8392 5202 & 020 8487 9202
📠 020 8487 9202
e-mail: events@pro.gov.uk
web: www.pro.gov.uk/
dir: Underground - Kew Gardens

The National Archives houses one of the finest, most complete archives in Europe, comprising the records of the central government and law courts from the Norman Conquest to the present century. It is a mine of information and includes the Domesday Book.

Times Open all year, Mon, Wed & Fri, 9-4.45; Tue, 10-7; Thu, 9-7. Closed 1st wk in Dec, Sun & public holiday wknds.* Facilities ❷ ℗ ⊑ toilets for disabled shop ⊗

MORDEN

Morden Hall Park

Morden Hall Rd SM4 5JD

☎ 020 8417 8091 📠 020 8687 0094

e-mail: mordenhallpark@nationaltrust.org.uk

web: www.nationaltrust.org.uk

dir: A298 (Bushey Rd), right at 2nd lights into Martin Way. Morden Hall signed

A green oasis in the heart of South West London. A former deer park, with a network of waterways including meadow, wetland and woodland habitats. Also discover the picturesque rose garden with over 2000 roses, fragrant from May to September.

Times Open all year, daily, 8-6. (Cafe & shop open daily 10-5, Bookshop Mon-Fri 11-3, Sat-Sun 12-4) Facilities 🅿 ☕ 🍴 licensed 🎪 (outdoor) toilets for disabled shop ♿

TWICKENHAM

Orleans House Gallery

Riverside TW1 3DJ

☎ 020 8831 6000 📠 020 8744 0501

e-mail: m.denovellis@richmond.gov.uk

web: www.richmond.gov.uk

dir: Richmond road (A305), Orleans Rd is on right just past Orleans Park School

Stroll beside the Thames and through the woodland gardens of Orleans House, where you will find stunning 18th-century interior design and an excellent public art gallery. Visitors of all ages can try out their own artistic talents in pre-booked workshops, and wide-ranging temporary exhibitions are held throughout the year - please telephone for details.

Times Open all year, Apr-Sep Tue-Sat 1-5.30, Sun & BH 2-5.30; Oct-Mar, Tue-Sat 1-4.30, Sun & BH 2-4.30* Facilities 🅿 🅿 🎪 toilets for disabled shop ⊗

LIVERPOOL

Central Library

William Brown St L3 8EW

☎ 0151 233 3000 📄 0151 233 5886
e-mail: refhum.central.library@liverpool.gov.uk
web: www.liverpool.gov.uk/libraries
dir: located between museum and art gallery-in the Cultural Quarter and part of the World Heritage Site

The Picton, Hornby and Brown buildings, situated in the Victorian grandeur of William Brown Street, house Liverpool's collection of over one million books, forming one of Britain's largest and oldest public libraries. The Liverpool Record Office is one of the country's largest and most significant County Record offices. Regular exhibitions of treasures from the collections are held, please telephone or see website for details.

Times Open all year, Mon-Fri 9-6, Sat 10-4 & Sun 12-4. Closed BHs.* Facilities ℗ ♿ (partly accessible) (Ground floor access - lift to floors 1-4 only) toilets for disabled ⊗

LIVERPOOL

International Slavery Museum

Albert Dock L3 4AQ

☎ 0151 478 4499 📄 0151 478 4590
web: www.liverpoolmuseums.org.uk
dir: enter Albert Dock from the Strand

2007 saw the bicentenary of the abolition of the slave trade in Britain, and this museum was opened at Albert Dock. It looks at the impact of the transatlantic slave trade and includes thought-provoking displays on issues such as freedom, identity, human rights, racial discrimination and cultural change.

Times Open all year, daily 10-5 & 24 Dec 10-2. Closed 25-26 Dec & 1 Jan.* Facilities ❷ ℗ ☕ ⑪ licensed toilets for disabled shop ⊗

LIVERPOOL

Merseyside Maritime Museum

Albert Dock L3 4AQ

☎ 0151 478 4499　🖹 0151 478 4590

web: www.liverpoolmuseums.org.uk

dir: enter Albert Dock from the Strand

Discover the story behind one of the world's greatest ports and the people who used it. For many, Liverpool was a gateway to a new life in other countries. For others its importance to the slave trade had less happy consequences. From slavers to luxury liners, submarine hunters to passenger ferries, explore Liverpool's central role.

Times Open all year, daily 10-5 & 24 Dec 10-2. Closed 25-26 Dec & 1 Jan.* Facilities 🅿 ⊡ ⦿ licensed 🎄 (outdoor) toilets for disabled shop ⊗

LIVERPOOL

Museum of Liverpool Life

Pier Head L3 4AA

☎ 0151 478 4080　🖹 0151 478 4090

dir: follow signs for Albert Dock, museum is on Pier Head side

The Museum of Liverpool Life celebrates the contribution of the people of Liverpool to national life. Recently expanded to include three new galleries, City Lives exploring the richness of Liverpool's cultural diversity, The River Room featuring life around the river Mersey and City Soldiers about the King's Regiment. Other galleries include Mersey Culture from Brookside to the Grand National, Making a Living and Demanding a Voice.

Times Open all year, daily 10-5. Closed from 2 on 24 Dec and all day 25-26 Dec & 1 Jan)* Facilities 🅿 🅿 🎄 indoor/outdoor toilets for disabled shop ⊗

77

LIVERPOOL

National Conservation Centre

Whitechapel L1 6HZ

☎ 0151 478 4999 📄 0151 478 4990

web: www.liverpoolmuseums.org.uk

dir: follow brown tourist signs to Whitechapel

Award-winning centre, the only one of its kind, gives the public an insight into the world of museum and gallery conservation. There is a regular changing exhibition programme.

Times Open all year, daily 10-5 & 24 Dec 10-2. Closed 25-26 Dec & 1 Jan. Facilities 🅿 🅟 ☕ 🚻 toilets for disabled shop ⊗

LIVERPOOL

Sudley House

Mossley Hill Rd L18 8BX

☎ 0151 724 3245

web: www.liverpoolmuseums.org.uk

dir: near Aigburth Station and Mossley Hill Station

Sudley, Liverpool's hidden gem, is unique, a Victorian merchant's house with an art collection displayed in its original setting. Works on show include paintings by Landseer and Turner, major pre-Raphaelite pictures and a group of 18th-century portraits by Gainsborough, Reynolds, Romney and Lawrence. Sudley houses an introductory display telling the history of the house, a Toy Zone (a display of dolls, toys and doll's house with a children's activities area), a display of items from the historic costume and fashion collection, and a new temporary exhibition gallery.

Times Open all year, daily 10-5 & 24 Dec 10-2. Closed 25-26 Dec & 1 Jan.* Facilities 🅿 ☕ 🚻 shop ⊗

LIVERPOOL

Tate Liverpool

Albert Dock L3 4BB
☎ 0151 702 7400 & 7402
🖷 0151 702 7401
e-mail: visiting.liverpool@tate.org.uk
web: www.tate.org.uk/liverpool/
dir: within walking distance of Liverpool Lime
Street train station, on the Albert Dock. Follow the
brown tourist signs from motorway.

Tate Liverpool is one of the largest galleries of
modern and contemporary art outside London
and is housed in a converted warehouse in the
historic Albert Dock. The gallery is home to the
National Collection of Modern Art in the North,
and has four floors displaying work selected from
the Tate Collection, as well as special exhibitions
which bring together artwork loaned from around
the world.

Times Open all year, Tue-Sun, BH Mon & all
Mons in Jun-Aug, 10-5.50. Closed 24-26 Dec &
Good Fri Fees Admission free. Charge for special
exhibitions, phone for details. Facilities Ⓟ ⟐
& toilets for disabled shop ⊗

LIVERPOOL

Walker Art Gallery

William Brown St L3 8EL
☎ 0151 478 4199 🖷 0151 478 4190
web: www.liverpoolmuseums.org.uk
dir: city centre adjacent to St George's Hall &
Lime St

The National Gallery of the North, this is one of
the finest art galleries in Europe, housing an
outstanding collection of British and European
art from the 14th to the 20th century. Many
visitors will already be familiar with some of the
much-loved paintings in the gallery's permanent
collection, including the tense Civil War scene
And when did you last see your father? and the
famous Tudor portraits. There are also temporary
exhibitions and a programme of special events,
please see the website for details.

Times Open all year, daily 10-5 & 24 Dec 10-2.
Closed 25-26 Dec & 1 Jan.* Facilities Ⓞ Ⓟ ⟐
†◎† licensed & toilets for disabled shop ⊗

LIVERPOOL

World Museum Liverpool

William Brown St L3 8EN

☎ 0151 478 4393 📠 0151 478 4350

web: www.liverpoolmuseums.org.uk

dir: in city centre next to St George's Hall and Lime St, follow brown signs

The World Museum Liverpool offers a journey of discovery from the oceans to the stars. Collections cover natural and physical sciences, ancient history and archaeology, and there are also frequently changing exhibitions, special events and other permanent attractions, such as the Bug House.

Times Open all year, daily 10-5 & 24 Dec 10-2. Closed 25-26 Dec & 1 Jan.* Facilities 🅿 🅟 ☕ 🍽 licensed 🍴 (indoor) ♿ toilets for disabled shop ⌾

PORT SUNLIGHT

Lady Lever Art Gallery

CH62 5EQ

☎ 0151 478 4136 📠 0151 478 4140

web: www.liverpoolmuseums.org.uk

dir: M53 junct 4 or from Liverpool/Birkenhead tunnel follow A41 towards Port Sunlight & follow brown heritage signs

The Lady Lever Art Gallery is one of the most beautiful galleries in the country and the perfect place to introduce younger members of the family to art. Home to the extensive personal collection of founder William Hesketh Lever, first Lord Leverhulme, this wonderful gallery is best known for its outstanding Victorian and pre-Raphaelite paintings by artists such as Leighton and Rossetti as well as other treasures just waiting to be discovered around every corner.

Times Open all year, daily 10-5 & 24 Dec 10-2. Closed 25-26 Dec & 1 Jan. Facilities 🅿 🅟 ☕ ♿ toilets for disabled shop ⌾

PRESCOT

Prescot Museum

34 Church St L34 3LA

☎ 0151 430 7787   📄 0151 430 7219

e-mail: prescot.museum.dlcs@knowsley.gov.uk

web: www.knowsley.gov.uk/leisure

dir: situated on corner of High St (A57) & Church St. Follow brown heritage signs

Permanent exhibitions reflecting the local history of the area, including its important clock and watch making heritage. There is a programme of special exhibitions, events and holiday activities, telephone for details.

Times Open all year, Tue-Sat 10-5 (closed 1-2), Sun 2-5. Closed BHs. Mon by appointment*
Facilities ℗ ♿ (partly accessible) (wheelchair access to ground floor) shop ⊗

SOUTHPORT

Atkinson Art Gallery

Lord St PR8 1DH

☎ 0151 934 2110   📄 0151 934 2109

e-mail: atkinson.gallery@leisure.sefton.gov.uk

web: www.seftonarts.co.uk

dir: located in centre of Lord St, next to Town Hall

The gallery specialises in 19th-and 20th-century oil paintings, watercolours, drawings and prints, as well as 20th-century sculpture. Temporary exhibitions are shown regularly at the art gallery, and there is also a 'painting of the month' talk.

Times Open all year, Tue-Thu 10-5, Fri 12-5, Sat 10-5. Closed Mon.* Facilities ℗ ♿ (partly accessible) (no access to temporary exhibition space second floor) shop ⊗

BACONSTHORPE

Baconsthorpe Castle

NR25 6LN

☎ 01799 322399

web: www.english-heritage.org.uk

dir: 0.75m N of Baconsthorpe off unclass road, 3m E of Holt

The remains of a 15th-century castle, built by Sir John Heydon during the Wars of the Roses. The exact date when the building was started is not known, since Sir John did not apply for the statutory royal licence necessary to construct a fortified house. In the 1560s, Sir John's grandson added the outer gatehouse, which was inhabited until the 1920s, when one of the turrets fell down. The remains of red brick and knapped flint are reflected in the lake, which partly embraces the castle as a moat.

Times Open at any reasonable time.*

Facilities 🅿 ⛭

BURGH CASTLE

Burgh Castle

NR31 9PZ

web: www.english-heritage.org.uk

dir: at far W end of Breydon Water on unclass road, 3m W of Great Yarmouth

Burgh Castle was built in the third century AD by the Romans, as one of a chain of forts along the Saxon Shore - the coast where Saxon invaders landed. Sections of the massive walls still stand.

Times Open at any reasonable time.*

Facilities ⊗ ⛭

CAISTER-ON-SEA

Caister Roman Site

web: www.english-heritage.org.uk
dir: 3m N of Great Yarmouth

The name Caister has Roman origins, and this was in fact a Roman naval base. The remains include the south gateway, a town wall built of flint with brick courses and part of what may have been a seamen's hostel.

Times Open at any reasonable time.*
Facilities ⊗ ♯

CROMER

RNLI Henry Blogg Museum

The Rocket House, The Gangway NR27 9ET
☎ 01263 511294 📄 01263 513047
e-mail: cromer_museum@rnli.org.uk
web: www.org.uk/henryblogg
dir: located at the bottom of East Gangway

A lifeboat has been stationed at Cromer since 1804, and the museum at the bottom of The Gangway covers local lifeboat history and the RNLI in general. The main exhibit is the WWII Watson Class lifeboat H F Bailey, the boat Henry Blogg coxed. In ten years he helped to save over 500 lives, and is still the RNLI's most decorated crew member. The exhibition hosts a number of new features including; interactive displays and radio/navigation instruction.

Times Open all year, Apr-Sep, Tue-Sun 10-5; Oct-Nov & Feb-Mar 10-4. Closed Dec-Jan.
Facilities ℗ ♿ toilets for disabled shop ⊗

KING'S LYNN

African Violet Centre

Terrington St Clement PE34 4PL
☎ 01553 828374 📠 01553 828376
e-mail:
manager@africanvioletandgardencentre.com
web: www.africanvioletandgardencentre.com
dir: situated beside A17 5m from Kings Lynn and
3m from A47/A17 junct

A warm and friendly welcome awaits you at the
African Violet Centre. As a major plant specialist
the centre offers a wide variety of plants for any
enthusiast. The African Violet Centre is a winner
of many Chelsea Gold Medals.

Times Open all year Mon-Sat 9-5, Sun 10-5.
Closed Xmas & New Year.* Facilities ℗ ☕
toilets for disabled shop ⊗

KING'S LYNN

King's Lynn Arts Centre

St George's Guildhall, 29 King St PE30 1HA
☎ 01553 765565 📠 01553 762141
e-mail: entertainment_admin@west-norfolk.
gov.uk
web: www.kingslynnarts.co.uk
dir: located just off Tuesday Market Place in King
Street, next to Globe Hotel

Although it has been used for many purposes,
the theatrical associations of this 15th-century
Guildhall are strongest: Shakespeare himself
is said to have performed here. A year round
programme of film, performing and visual arts
takes place. Contact box office on 01553 764864
for details.

Times Open all year Mon-Fri, 10-4. Closed on
BHs, Good Fri & 24 Dec-1st Mon in Jan. Coffee
shop open Mon-Sat 9.30-5. Riverside Restaurant
Mon-Sat 12-2 & 6.30-9.30. Facilities ℗ ☕
🍽 licensed ♿ (partly accessible) (steps to
restaurant) ⊗ ♨

NORTH CREAKE

Creake Abbey

NR21 9LF
web: www.english-heritage.org.uk
dir: off B1355

The ruins of the church of an Augustinian abbey,
later converted to an almshouse.

Times Open at any reasonable time.*
Facilities ⊗ ♯

NORWICH

Sainsbury Centre for Visual Arts

University of East Anglia NR4 7TJ
☎ 01603 593199 📄 01603 591053
e-mail: scva@uea.ac.uk
web: www.scva.ac.uk
dir: A47 bypass W towards Swaffham. 1st exit
onto B1108, follow brown signs

The collection of Sir Robert and Lady Sainsbury
was given to the University in 1973. This
outstanding collection is housed in two buildings
designed by Norman Foster and combines modern
Western art with fine and applied arts from
Africa, the Pacific, the Americas, Asia, Egypt,
Medieval Europe and the ancient Mediterranean.

Times Open all year, Tue-Sun 10-5, Wed
10-8 Fees Permanent collection free, special
exhibitions £4 (concessions £2).* Facilities 🅿
⊡ ⦿ licensed ㅠ (indoor & outdoor) ♿ toilets
for disabled shop ⊗

ST OLAVES

St Olave's Priory

web: www.english-heritage.org.uk
dir: 5.5m SW of Great Yarmouth on A143

Remains of an Augustinian priory founded nearly 2000 years after the death in 1030 of the patron saint of Norway, after whom it was named.

Times Open at any reasonable time.*
Facilities ⌗

THETFORD

Thetford Priory

web: www.english-heritage.org.uk
dir: on W side of Thetford near station

A glimpse of medieval religious life before the dissolution of the monasteries. The Priory of Our Lady of Thetford belonged to the Order of Cluny, and was founded in 1103 by Roger Bigod, an old soldier and friend of William the Conqueror.

Times Open all year at any reasonable time.*
Facilities ⌗

THETFORD

Thetford Warren Lodge

web: www.english-heritage.org.uk
dir: 2m W of Thetford, off B1107

The remains of a two-storey hunting lodge, built in the 15th-century of flint with stone dressings.

Times Open at any reasonable time.*
Facilities ⌗

WEETING

Weeting Castle

IP27 0RQ
web: www.english-heritage.org.uk
dir: 2m N of Brandon off B1106

This ruined 11th-century fortified manor house stands in a moated enclosure. There are interesting but slight remains of a three-storey cross-wing.

Times Open at any reasonable time.*
Facilities ⌗

KETTERING

Alfred East Art Gallery

Sheep St NN16 0AN

☎ 01536 534274

e-mail: museumandgallery@kettering.gov.uk

web: www.kettering.gov.uk/art

dir: A43/A14, located in town centre, next to library, 5 min walk from railway station

The Gallery has a permanent exhibition space showing work by Sir Alfred East, Thomas Cooper Gotch and other local artists, as well as selections from the Gallery's contemporary collection. Two further display spaces are dedicated to temporary changing exhibitions of art, craft and photography by regional and national artists. There is also a monthly lunchtime talks programme and regular family events.

Times Open all year, Tue-Sat 9.30-5 (closed BHs) Facilities ℗ ⨅ (outdoor) ♿ (partly accessible) (wheelchair access via Kettering Library, during gallery opening hrs) shop ⊗

NORTHAMPTON

Northampton Museum & Art Gallery

Guildhall Rd NN1 1DP

☎ 01604 838111 📠 01604 838720

e-mail: museums@northampton.gov.uk

web: www.northampton.gov.uk/museums

dir: situated in town centre, in Guildhall Rd

Home to the world's largest collection of shoes, Northampton Museum and Art Gallery displays shoes that have been in fashion through the ages, from Ferragamo to Vivienne Westwood. 'Life and Sole' tells the history of footwear, and other displays detail the history of Northampton, and British and Oriental ceramics and glass. There is also a gallery of Italian paintings depicting scenes from the Bible and ancient mythology. There is a changing programme of exhibitions.

Times Open all year, Tue-Sat 10-5, Sun 2-5. (closed 25-26 Dec & 1 Jan). Facilities ℗ ♿ toilets for disabled shop ⊗

CARRAWBROUGH

Temple of Mithras (Hadrian's Wall)

web: www.english-heritage.org.uk
dir: 3.75m W of Chollerford on B6318

This fascinating Mithraic temple was uncovered by a farmer in 1949. Its three altars to the war god Mithras, date from the third century AD, and are now in the Museum of Antiquities in Newcastle, but there are copies on site.

Times * Facilities ⓟ ⌗

MORPETH

Morpeth Chantry Bagpipe Museum

Bridge St NE61 1PD

☎ 01670 500717 🖹 01670 500710
e-mail: anne.moore@castlemorpeth.gov.uk
dir: off A1, in Morpeth town centre

This unusual museum specialises in the history and development of Northumbrian small pipes and their music. They are set in the context of bagpipes from around the world, from India to Inverness. It is also host to the Morpeth Northumbrian Gathering, with music and crafts the weekend after Easter and a traditional music festival through the month of October.

Times Open all year, Mon-Sat 9.30-5, open Sun in Aug & Dec. Closed 25-26 Dec, 1 Jan & Etr Mon.*
Facilities ⓟ ♿ (partly accessible) (lift to 1st floor) toilets for disabled shop

NORHAM

Norham Castle

TD15 2JY

☎ 01289 382329

web: www.english-heritage.org.uk

A mighty border fortress built in 1160, was one of the strongest of the border castles. Take an audio tour conjuring up four centuries of sieges and war with the Scots.

Times Open 21 Mar-Sep, Sat-Sun & BH. Admission limited. Please call 01289 304493 for details.* Facilities ℗ ⊗ ⧫

EDWINSTOWE

Sherwood Forest Country Park & Visitor Centre

NG21 9HN

☎ 01623 823202 & 824490

📄 01623 823202

e-mail: sherwood.forest@nottscc.gov.uk

web:

www.nottinghamshire.gov.uk/sherwoodforestcp

dir: on B6034 N of Edwinstowe between A6075 and A616

At the heart of the Robin Hood legend is Sherwood Forest. Today it is a country park and visitor centre with 450 acres of ancient oaks and shimmering silver birches. Waymarked pathways guide you through the forest. A year round programme of events includes the spectacular annual Robin Hood Festival.

Times Open all year. Country Park: open daily dawn to dusk. Visitor Centre: open daily 10-5 (4.30 Nov-Mar). Closed 25 Dec.* Facilities ℗ ℗ ⊑ 禾 (outdoor) toilets for disabled shop

NEWARK-ON-TRENT

Newark Millgate Museum

48 Millgate NG24 4TS
☎ 01636 655730   📄 01636 655735
e-mail: museums@nsdc.info
web: www.newark-sherwooddc.gov.uk/museums
dir: easy access from A1 & A46

The museum is home to diverse social history collections and features fascinating exhibitions - recreated streets, shops and houses in period settings. There are also children's activities. The mezzanine gallery, home to a number of temporary exhibitions shows the work of local artists, designers and photographers.

Times Open all year, Apr-Sep, Tue-Sun, 10.30-4.30; Oct-Mar, Tue-Fri, 10.30-4, Sat-Sun 1-4. Open spring and summer BH Mon. Facilities Ⓟ ♈⛟& (partly accessible) (access to ground floor only for wheelchair users) toilets for disabled shop ⊗

NOTTINGHAM

The Lace Centre

Severns Building, Castle Rd NG1 6AA
☎ 0115 941 3539   📄 0115 941 3539
dir: follow signs for Castle, situated opposite Robin Hood statue

Exquisite Nottingham lace fills this small 14th-century building to capacity, with panels also hanging from the beamed ceiling. There are weekly demonstrations of lace-making on Thursday afternoons from Easter to October. Telephone for details.

Times Open all year, Jan-Mar, daily 10-4; Apr-Oct, 10-5; Nov-Dec, 10-4. Every Sun 11-4. Phone for Xmas & New Year.* Facilities Ⓟ shop

BANBURY

Banbury Museum

Spiceball Park Rd OX16 2PQ

☎ 01295 259855 📠 01295 269469

e-mail: banburymuseum@cherwell-dc.gov.uk

web: www.cherwell-dc.gov.uk/banburymuseum

dir: M40 junct 11 straight across at first rdbt into Hennef Way, left at next rdbt into Concord Ave, right at next rdbt & left at next rdbt, Castle Quay Shopping Centre & Museum on right

The Banbury Museum is situated in an attractive canal-side location in the centre of Banbury. Exciting modern displays tell of Banbury's origins and historic past. The Civil War; the plush manufacturing industry; the Victorian market town; costume from the 17th century to the present day; Tooley's Boatyard and the Oxford Canal, are just some of the subjects illustrated in the new museum.

Times Open all year, Mon-Sat, 10-5.
Facilities ℗ 🍽 licensed ♿ toilets for disabled shop ⊗

DEDDINGTON

Deddington Castle

OX5 4TE

web: www.english-heritage.org.uk

dir: S of B4031 on E side of Deddington

The large earthworks of the outer and inner baileys can be seen, and the remains of 12th-century castle buildings have been excavated, but they are not now visible.

Times Open any reasonable time.* Facilities ⊞

MINSTER LOVELL

Minster Lovell Hall & Dovecote

OX8 5RN

web: www.english-heritage.org.uk
dir: adjacent to Minster Lovell Church, 3m W of
Witney off A40

Home of the ill-fated Lovell family, the ruins of
the 15th-century house are steeped in history and
legend. One of the main features of the estate is
the medieval dovecote.

Times Open any reasonable time. Dovecote-
exterior only* Facilities ⛶

NORTH LEIGH

North Leigh Roman Villa

OX8 6QB

web: www.english-heritage.org.uk
dir: 2m N of North Leigh

This is the remains of a large and well-build
Roman courtyard villa. The most important
feature is an almost complete mosaic tile floor,
which is intricately patterned in reds and browns.

Times Grounds open any reasonable time.
Viewing window for mosaic tile floor. (Pedestrian
access only from main road).* Facilities 🅿 ⛶

OXFORD

Ashmolean Museum of Art & Archaeology

Beaumont St OX1 2PH

☎ 01865 278000 📄 01865 278018
web: www.ashmolean.org
dir: city centre, opposite The Randolph Hotel

The oldest museum in the country, opened in 1683, the Ashmolean contains Oxford University's priceless collections. Many important historical art pieces and artefacts are on display, including work from Ancient Greece through to the twentieth century. The museum has undergone a massive redevelopment, including the building of 39 new galleries, an education centre, conservation studios and a walkway.

Times Open all year, Tue-Sun 10-5, BH Mons 10-5. Closed during St.Giles Fair (7-9 Sept) Xmas & 1 Jan. Facilities ℗ 🖵 🍴 licensed ♿ toilets for disabled shop ⊗

OXFORD

Museum of Oxford

St Aldate's OX1 1DZ

☎ 01865 252761 📄 01865 252555
e-mail: museum@oxford.gov.uk
web: www.museumofoxford.org.uk

Permanent displays depict the archaeology and history of the city through the ages. There are temporary exhibitions, facilities for school parties and groups, and an audio tour. A programme of family, community events and activities also operates throughout the year.

Times Open all year, Tue-Fri 10-5, Sat & Sun 12-5. Closed 25-26 Dec.* Facilities 🖵 ♿ (partly accessible) (main entrance steps, alternative access to ground floor via Town Hall next door) toilets for disabled shop ⊗

OXFORD

Museum of the History of Science

Broad St OX1 3AZ

☎ 01865 277280 📠 01865 277288

e-mail: museum@mhs.ox.ac.uk

web: www.mhs.ox.ac.uk

dir: next to Sheldonian Theatre in city centre, on Broad St

The first purpose-built museum in Britain, containing the world's finest collection of early scientific instruments used in astronomy, navigation, surveying, physics and chemistry. Various events through the year.

Times Open all year, Tue-Fri 12-5, Sat 10-5, Sun 2-5. Closed Xmas and Etr Sun. Facilities ℗ ♿ (partly accessible) (lift to basement) toilets for disabled shop ⊗

OXFORD

Oxford University Museum of Natural History

Parks Rd OX1 3PW

☎ 01865 272950 📠 01865 272970

e-mail: info@oum.ox.ac.uk

web: www.oum.ox.ac.uk

dir: opposite Keble College

Built between 1855 and 1860, this museum of "the natural sciences" was intended to satisfy a growing interest in biology, botany, archaeology, zoology, entomology and so on. The museum reflects Oxford University's position as a 19th-century centre of learning, with displays of early dinosaur discoveries, Darwinian evolution and Elias Ashmole's collection of preserved animals. Although visitors to the Pitt-Rivers Museum must pass through the University Museum, the two should not be confused. The museum celebrates its 150th Anniversary in 2010 see website for details.

Times Open daily 10-5. Times vary at Xmas & Etr. Facilities ℗ ⧗ (outdoor) ♿ toilets for disabled shop ⊗

OXFORD

Pitt Rivers Museum

South Parks Rd OX1 3PP
☎ 01865 270927 🖷 01865 270943
e-mail: prm@prm.ox.ac.uk
web: www.prm.ox.ac.uk
dir: 10 min walk from city centre, visitors entrance on Parks Rd through the Oxford University Museum of Natural History

The museum is one of the city's most popular attractions. It is part of the University of Oxford and was founded in 1884. The collections held at the museum are internationally acclaimed, and contain many objects from different cultures of the world and from various periods, all grouped by type, or purpose. The upper gallery, housing the weapons and armour displays, will be closed until Spring 2010.

Times Open all year, Tue-Sun & BH Mon 10-4.30, Mon 12-4.30. Contact museum at Christmas & Easter to check times. The upper gallery, housing the weapons and armour displays, will be closed until Spring 2010. Facilities ℗ ♿ toilets for disabled shop ⊗

OXFORD

St Edmund Hall

College of Oxford University OX1 4AR
☎ 01865 279000 🖷 01865 279090
e-mail: bursary@seh.ox.ac.uk
web: www.seh.ox.ac.uk
dir: Queen's Lane Oxford at end of High St

This is the only surviving medieval academic hall and has a Norman crypt, 17th-century dining hall, chapel and quadrangle. Other buildings are of the 18th and 20th centuries.

Times Open all year. Closed 20-30 Mar, 23-26 Aug, 21 Dec-5 Jan* Facilities ⊑ ♿ (partly accessible) toilets for disabled ⊗

UFFINGTON

Uffington Castle, White Horse & Dragon Hill

☎ 01793 762209
dir: S of B4507

The 'castle' is an Iron Age fort on the ancient Ridgeway Path. It covers about eight acres and has only one gateway. On the hill below the fort is the White Horse, a 375ft prehistoric figure carved in the chalk hillside and thought to be about 3000 years old.

Times Open at any reasonable time.*
Facilities ❷ ⊼ (outdoor) ♿ (partly accessible) (disabled car parking and access to view points) ❧

WOODSTOCK

Oxfordshire Museum

Fletcher's House, Park St OX20 1SN
☎ 01993 811456 🖹 01993 813239
e-mail: oxon.museum@oxfordshire.go.uk
web: www.tomocc.org.uk
dir: A44 Evesham-Oxford, follow signs for Blenheim Palace. Museum opposite church

Situated in the heart of the historic town of Woodstock, the award-winning redevelopment of Fletcher's House provides a home for the new county museum. Set in attractive gardens, the new museum celebrates Oxfordshire in all its diversity and features collections of local history, art, archaeology, landscape and wildlife as well as a gallery exploring the County's innovative industries from nuclear power to nanotechnology. Interactive exhibits offer new learning experiences for visitors of all ages. The museum's purpose-built Garden Gallery houses a variety of touring exhibitions of regional and national interest. A new display of dinosaur footprints from Ardley Quarry and a replica megalosaurus, are located in the walled garden.

Times Open all year, Tue-Sat 10-5, Sun 2-5. Closed Good Fri, 25-26 Dec & 1 Jan. Galleries closed on Mon, but open BH Mons, 2-5.
Facilities ❷ ⊑ ⑩ licensed ⊼ (outdoor) ♿ toilets for disabled shop ⊗

OAKHAM

Oakham Castle

Catmos St LE15 6HW
☎ 01572 758440 ▤ 01572 758445
e-mail: museum@rutland.gov.uk
web: www.rutland.gov.uk/castle
dir: off Market Place

An exceptionally fine Norman Great Hall built in the 12th century. Earthworks, walls and remains of an earlier motte can be seen along with medieval sculptures and unique presentation horseshoes forfeited by peers of the realm and royalty to the Lord of the Manor. The castle is now a popular place for civil marriages, meetings and special events.

Times Open all year, Mon-Sat 10.30-5 (closed 1-1.30), Sun 2-4. Closed Xmas, New Year & Good Fri* Facilities ℗ ♿ (partly accessible) shop ⊗

OAKHAM

Rutland County Museum & Visitor Centre

Catmos St LE15 6HW
☎ 01572 758440 ▤ 01572 758445
e-mail: museum@rutland.gov.uk
web: www.rutland.gov.uk/museum
dir: on A6003, S of town centre

Rutland County Museum is the perfect introduction to England's smallest county. The 'Welcome to Rutland' gallery is a guide to its history. The museum includes a shop and study area. On show in the 18th-century Riding School are displays of archaeology, history and an extensive rural life collection.

Times Open all year, Mon-Sat 10.30-5, Sun 2-4. Closed Xmas, New Year & Good Fri.*
Facilities ℗ ℗ ♿ (partly accessible) toilets for disabled shop ⊗

ACTON BURNELL

Acton Burnell Castle

SY5 7PE
web: www.english-heritage.org.uk
dir: in Acton Burnell on unclass road 8m S of
Shrewsbury

Not so much a castle, more a fortified 13th-century manor house, Acton Burnell Castle is now just a shell, but it is believed that the first parliament at which the commons were fully represented was held here in 1283.

Times Open at all reasonable times.*
Facilities ⊞

BOSCOBEL

Whiteladies Priory

web: www.english-heritage.org.uk
dir: 1m SW of Boscobel House, off an unclass
road between A41 and A5

Only the ruins are left of this Augustinian nunnery, which dates from 1158 and was destroyed in the Civil War. After the Battle of Worcester Charles II hid here and in the nearby woods before going on to Boscobel House.

Times Open 21 Mar-Oct, daily 10-5. Closed Nov-Mar.* Facilities ⊞

COSFORD

The Royal Air Force Museum

TF11 8UP

☎ 01902 376200 📄 01902 376211

e-mail: cosford@rafmuseum.org

web: www.rafmuseum.org

dir: on A41, 1m S of M54 junct 3

The Royal Air Force Museum Cosford has one of the largest aviation collections in the UK, with 70 historic aircraft on display. Visitors will be able to see Britain's V bombers - Vulcan, Victor and Valiant and other aircraft suspended in flying attitudes in the national Cold War exhibition, housed in a landmark building covering 8000sqm.

Times Open all year daily, 10-6 (last admission 4). Closed 24-26 Dec & 1 Jan, 7-11 Jan.* Facilities 🅿 💻 🍴 licensed 🎏 (outdoor) ♿ toilets for disabled shop ⊗

LILLESHALL

Lilleshall Abbey

TF10 9HW

☎ 0121 625 6820

web: www.english-heritage.org.uk

dir: off A518 on unclass road

In the beautiful grounds of Lilleshall Hall, ruined Lilleshall Abbey was founded shortly before the middle of the 12th century and from the high west front visitors can look down the entire 228ft length of the abbey church.

Times Open 21 Mar-Sep, daily 10-5. Closed Oct-Mar.* Facilities ▦

MORETON CORBET

Moreton Corbet Castle

web: www.english-heritage.org.uk
dir: In Moreton Corbet off B5063 (a turning off A49), 7 miles NE of Shrewsbury

Inherited by the Corbets in 1235, who are thought to have remodelled the great keep, this castle may already have been standing for over 100 years. It was remodelled in the 16th century and then partially demolished to make way for a great Elizabethan mansion. Although damaged in the Civil War, the castle and mansion stand today as one of the most picturesque ruins of the Shropshire Marches.

Times Open at any reasonable time.*
Facilities ⓟ ♯

OSWESTRY

Old Oswestry Hill Fort

web: www.english-heritage.org.uk
dir: 1m N of Oswestry, off an unclass road off A483

An impressive Iron Age hill-fort of 68 acres, defended by a series of five ramparts, with an elaborate western entrance and unusual earthwork cisterns.

Times Open at any reasonable time.*
Facilities ♯

NUNNEY

Nunney Castle

web: www.english-heritage.org.uk
dir: 3.5m SW of Frome, off A361

Built in 1373, and supposedly modelled on
France's Bastille, this crenellated manor house
has one of the deepest moats in England. It was
ruined by Parliamentarian forces in the Civil War.

Times Open at any reasonable time.*
Facilities ⊞

STOKE ST GREGORY

Willow & Wetlands Visitor Centre

Meare Green Court TA3 6HY
☎ 01823 490249 📄 01823 490814
e-mail: info@englishwillowbaskets.co.uk
web: www.englishwillowbaskets.co.uk
dir: between North Curry & Stoke St Gregory,
signed from A361 & A378

The centre is owned and run by Somerset
Basketmakers and willow growers P H Coate
& Son. The environmental exhibition gives a
fascinating insight into the Somerset Levels and
Moors. Optional guided tours are available during
the week.

Times Open all year incl BHs, daily (ex Sun)
9.30-5. Optional guided tours are available
weekdays at 11am & 2pm (charged).*
Facilities ❷ ⊒ 尹 (outdoor) ⅋ (partly
accessible) (some areas of the garden
inaccessible) toilets for disabled shop

STOKE-SUB-HAMDON

Stoke-Sub-Hamdon Priory

North St TA4 6QP
☎ 01935 823289
web: www.nationaltrust.org.uk
dir: between A303 & A3088

A complex of buildings, begun in the 14th century for the priests of the Chantry Chapel of St Nicholas (now destroyed).

Times Open 13 Mar-Oct, daily 10-6 or dusk if earlier. Facilities ⓟ ♿ (partly accessible) (steps & rough ground) ⊗ � 🜚

STREET

The Shoe Museum

C & J Clark Ltd, High St BA16 0EQ
☎ 01458 842169   📄 01458 442226
e-mail: linda.stevens@clarks.com
dir: A39 to Street, follow signs for Clarks Village

The museum is in the oldest part of the shoe factory set up by Cyrus and James Clark in 1825. It contains shoes from Roman times to the present, buckles, engravings, fashion plates, machinery, hand tools and advertising material.

Times Open all year, Mon-Fri 10-4.45. Closed over Christmas, BH & weekends. Facilities ⓟ ♿ shop ⊗

HALFPENNY GREEN

Halfpenny Green Vineyards

DY7 5EP

☎ 01384 221122 📠 01384 221101
e-mail:
enquiries@halfpenny-green-vineyards.co.uk
web: www.halfpenny-green-vineyards.co.uk
dir: 0.5m off B4176 Dudley to Telford road

Using German, French and hybrid varieties that can prosper even in the poorest British summer, this vineyard offers "The complete English wine experience." This includes a self-guided vineyard trail as well as guided tours, wine-tasting, a craft centre and a visitor centre. Visitors can purchase wines with personalised labels for special occasions. Coarse fishing is also available.

Times Open all year, daily 10-5.* Facilities 🅿 🍽 ⌑ licensed ♿ toilets for disabled shop ⊗

LICHFIELD

Samuel Johnson Birthplace Museum

Breadmarket St WS13 6LG

☎ 01543 264972 📠 01543 258441
e-mail: sjmuseum@lichfield.gov.uk
web: www.samueljohnsonbirthplace.org.uk
dir: located in city centre market place

Dr Samuel Johnson, author of the famous English dictionary of 1755, lexicographer, poet, critic, biographer and personality was born in this house in 1709. The birthplace now houses a museum dedicated to his extraordinary life, work and personality. Five floors of exhibits featuring period room settings, introductory video and personal items owned by Johnson, his family and his famous friends. Johnson's birthday is celebrated annually in September. Please see the website for special events.

Times Open all year, daily Apr-Sep 10.30-4.30; Oct-Mar 11-3.30. Facilities ℗ ♿ (partly accessible) (Grade 1 listed & many unavoidable stairs) shop ⊗

STAFFORD

Shire Hall Gallery

Market Square ST16 2LD

☎ 01785 278345 📄 02785 278327

e-mail: shirehallgallery@staffordshire.gov.uk

web: www.staffordshire.gov.uk/sams

dir: In pedestrianised area of the town centre, 5 min walk from railway

With free entry and an exciting activities programme, there's something for everyone at the Shire Hall Gallery - Staffordshire's largest venue for contemporary arts and crafts. Visit the historic courtroom, or book a play session in the multi-sensory room. Contact the gallery for info on the latest exhibitions and activities.

Times Open all year, Mon & Wed-Sat 9.30-5; Tue 10-5; Sun 1-4. Gallery closes for exhibition changes and at BHs, please call for further details. Facilities ℗ 🍴 ♿ (partly accessible) (some areas only accessible by lift, limited wheelchair access to the Court room) toilets for disabled shop ⊗

STOKE-ON-TRENT

The Potteries Museum & Art Gallery

Bethesda St, Hanley ST1 3DW

☎ 01782 232323 📄 01782 232500

e-mail: museums@stoke.gov.uk

web: www.stoke.gov.uk/museums

dir: M6 junct 15/16 take A500 to Stoke-on-Trent. Follow signs for city centre (Hanley), Cultural Quarter & The Potteries Museum

The history of the Potteries under one roof, including a dazzling display of the world's finest collection of Staffordshire ceramics. Other displays introduce natural, local and archaeological history from in and around The Potteries, and a Mark 16 Spitfire commemorating its locally born designer - Reginald Mitchell.

Times Open all year, Mar-Oct, Mon-Sat 10-5, Sun 2-5; Nov-Feb, Mon-Sat 10-4, Sun 1-4. Closed 25 Dec-1 Jan.* Facilities ℗ ℗ 🍴 toilets for disabled shop ⊗

WALL

Wall Roman Site

Watling St WS14 0AW
☎ 01543 480768
web: www.english-heritage.org.uk
dir: off A5

Explore the haunting remains of a 2,000 year old wayside staging post situated along Watling Street, the famous Kent to North Wales Roman road.

Times Site open: Mar-Oct, daily 10-5; Museum 21 Mar-Oct, last Sun & Mon of each month 10-5. Closed Nov-Feb.* Facilities ℗ shop ♯ ✿

FLIXTON

Norfolk & Suffolk Aviation Museum

Buckeroo Way, The Street NR35 1NZ
☎ 01986 896644
e-mail: nsam.flixton@tesco.net
web: www.aviationmuseum.net
dir: off A143, take B1062, 2m W of Bungay

Situated in the Waveney Valley, the museum has over 60 historic aircraft. There is also a Bloodhound surface-to-air missile, the 446th Bomb Group Museum, RAF Bomber Command Museum, the Royal Observer Corps Museum, RAF Air-Sea Rescue and Coastal Command and a souvenir shop. Among the displays are Decoy Sites and Wartime Deception, Fallen Eagles - Wartime Luftwaffe Crashes and an ex-Ipswich airport hangar made by Norwich company Boulton and Paul Ltd.

Times Open all year, Apr-Oct, Sun-Thu 10-5 (last admission 4); Nov-Mar, Tue, Wed & Sun 10-4 (last admission 3). Closed late Dec-early Jan.* Facilities ℗ ℗ � ⊼ (outdoor) ঙ toilets for disabled shop ⊗

IPSWICH

Christchurch Mansion

Soane St IP4 2BE
☎ 01473 433554 & 213761
🖹 01473 433564
e-mail: museums.service@ipswich.gov.uk
web: www.ipswich.gov.uk
dir: S side of Christchurch Park, close to town centre

The house was built in 1548 on the site of an Augustinian priory. Set in a beautiful park, it displays period rooms and an art gallery which has changing exhibitions. The Suffolk Artists' Gallery has a collection of paintings by Constable and Gainsborough.

Times Open all year, Mon-Sun 10-5. Closed Good Fri, 24-26 Dec & 1 Jan.* Facilities ℗ � ⚐ &
(partly accessible) toilets for disabled shop ⊗

IPSWICH

Ipswich Museum

High St IP1 3QH
☎ 01473 433550 🖹 01473 433558
e-mail: museum.service@ipswich.gov.uk
web: www.ipswich.gov.uk
dir: follow tourist signs to Crown St car park. Museum 3 mins walk

The Museum has sections on Victorian Natural History, Suffolk wildlife, Suffolk geology, Roman Suffolk, Anglo-Saxon Ipswich and Peoples of the World. There is also one of the best bird collections in the country.

Times Open all year, Tue-Sat 10-5. Closed Sun, Mon, Good Friday, 24-26 Dec & 1 Jan.*
Facilities ℗ & toilets for disabled shop ⊗

LEISTON

Leiston Abbey

IP16 4TD

☎ 01728 831354 & 832500

🖹 01728 635378

e-mail: admin@leistonabbey.co.uk

web: www.leistonabbey.co.uk

dir: N of Leiston, off B1069

For hundreds of years this 14th-century abbey was used as a farm and its church became a barn. A Georgian house, now used as a school for young musicians, was built into its fabric and remains of the choir, the church transepts and parts of the cloisters still stand.

Times Open at any reasonable time.*
Facilities 🅿 ♿ (partly accessible) (wheelchair access restricted in some areas) ⊗

LINDSEY

St James' Chapel (Lindsey)

Rose Green

web: www.english-heritage.org.uk

dir: on unclass road 0.5m E of Rose Green

Built mainly in the 13th century, this small thatched, flint-and-stone chapel incorporates some earlier work.

Times Open all year, daily 10-4.* Facilities ⊗ ⌗

ASH VALE

Army Medical Services Museum

Keogh Barracks GU12 5RQ

☎ 01252 868612   📄 01252 868832

e-mail: armymedicalmuseum@btinternet.com

web: www.ams-museum.org.uk

dir: M3 junct 4 on A331 to Mytchett then follow tourist signs

The museum traces the history of Army medicine, nursing, dentistry and veterinary science from 1660 until the present day. Medical equipment and ambulances complement displays including uniforms and medals.

Times Open all year, Mon-Fri 10-3.30. Closed Xmas, New Year & BH. Wknds by appointment only.* Facilities 🅿 Ⓟ toilets for disabled shop ⊗

GUILDFORD

Guildford House Gallery

155 High St GU1 3AJ

☎ 01483 444742   📄 01483 458563

e-mail: guildfordhouse@guildford.gov.uk

web: www.guildfordhouse.co.uk

dir: N side of High St, opposite Sainsbury's

An impressive building in its own right, Guildford House dates from 1660 and has been Guildford's art gallery since 1959. A changing selection from the Borough's Art Collection is on display, including pastel portraits by John Russell, topographical paintings and contemporary craftwork, as well as temporary exhibitions.

Times Open all year Tue-Sat 10-4.45. (Closed Good Fri & 25-26 Dec)* Facilities Ⓟ 🖵 🍽 licensed ♿ (partly accessible) shop ⊗

BRIGHTON

Booth Museum of Natural History

194 Dyke Rd BN1 5AA
☎ 01273 292777 📠 01273 292778
e-mail: boothmuseum@brighton-hove.gov.uk
web: www.virtualmuseum.info
dir: from A27 Brighton by pass, 1.5m NW of town centre, opposite Dyke Rd Park

The museum was built in 1874 to house the bird collection of Edward Thomas Booth (1840-1890). His collection is still on display, but the museum has expanded considerably since Booth's day and now includes thousands of butterfly and insect specimens, geology galleries with fossils, rocks and local dinosaur bones, a magnificent collection of animal skeletons, largely collected by the Brighton solicitor F W Lucas (1842-1932), and an interactive discovery gallery.

Times Open all year, Mon-Sat (ex Thu) 10-5, Sun 2-5. Closed Good Fri, Xmas & 1 Jan.
Facilities Ⓟ ♿ (partly accessible) (rear access, otherwise accessible) toilets for disabled shop ®

BRIGHTON

Brighton Museum & Art Gallery

Royal Pavilion Gardens BN1 1EE
☎ 03000 290900 📠 03000 290908
e-mail: museums@brighton-hove.gov.uk
web: www.brighton.virtualmuseum.info
dir: M23/A23 from London. In city centre near seafront. New entrance in Royal Pavilion Gardens

A £10 million redevelopment transformed Brighton Museum into a state-of-the-art visitor attraction. Dynamic and innovative galleries, including two new Egyptian galleries, fashion, 20th-century design and world art, feature exciting interactive displays appealing to all ages. The museum also benefits from a spacious entrance located in the Royal Pavilion gardens and full disabled access. See website for details of special events and exhibitions.

Times Open all year, Tue 10-7, Wed-Sat 10-5, Sun 2-5. (Closed Mon ex BHs 10-5). Fees Free admission (charge made for touring exhibitions).
Facilities Ⓟ ☕ ⛩ (outdoor) ♿ toilets for disabled shop ®

HASTINGS & ST LEONARDS

Old Town Hall Museum of Local History

Old Town Hall, High St TN34 1EW

☎ 01424 451052

e-mail: oldtownmuseum@hastings.gov.uk

web: www.hmag.org.uk

dir: off A259 coast road into High St in Hastings old town. Signed

Situated in the heart of Hastings Old Town, the museum was originally a Georgian Town Hall built in 1823. Refurbished displays tell the story of Hastings Old Town as a walk back in time, with features including a Cinque Ports ship, and interactive displays.

Times Open all year, Apr-Sep, Mon-Sat 10-5, Sun 11-5.; Oct-Mar, Mon-Fri 10-4, Sat & Sun 11-4. Facilities ℗ & toilets for disabled shop ⊗

HERSTMONCEUX

The Truggery

Coopers Croft BN27 1QL

☎ 01323 832314

e-mail: info@truggery.co.uk

web: www.truggery.co.uk

dir: from A22 at Hailsham, Boship rdbt, take A271 towards Bexhill for 4m

The art of Sussex trug making can be seen through all the work processes including preparing timber, use of the draw knife and assembly of trug. There is a wide selection of Sussex Trugs and locally made garden related items.

Times Open all year Thu-Sat 10-1, or by appointment.* Facilities ⊕ ℗ & (partly accessible) (path to workshop is over rough ground) shop

BRAMBER

Bramber Castle

BN4 3FB
web: www.english-heritage.org.uk
dir: on W side of village off A283

The remains of a Norman motte and bailey castle. The gatehouse (still standing almost to its original height) and walls are still visible.

Times Open any reasonable time.*
Facilities ℗ 👜

CHICHESTER

Chichester Cathedral

West St PO19 1PX
☎ 01243 782595 📄 01243 812499
e-mail: visitors@chichestercathedral.org.uk
web: www.chichestercathedral.org.uk
dir: in city centre

This magnificent 900 year old Cathedral combines the ancient and the modern, with treasures ranging from unique medieval carvings to world famous 20th century artworks.

Times Open end Mar-end Sep, daily 7.15-7; end Sep-end Mar 7.15-6. Fees Donations much appreciated. Facilities ℗ 🖵 🍴 licensed 🪑 (outdoor) ♿ toilets for disabled shop ⊗

HIGHDOWN

Highdown

Highdown Gardens BN12 6PE

☎ 01903 501054   🖹 01903 218757

e-mail: chris.beardsley@worthing.gov.uk

web: www.worthing.gov.uk/wbc

dir: N off A259 between Worthing & Littlehampton. Access off dual carriageway, when coming from E proceed to rdbt

Set on downland countryside this unique garden overlooks the sea, and has been deemed a National Collection due to the unique assortment of rare plants and trees. The garden was the achievement of Sir Frederick and Lady Stern, who worked for fifty years to prove that plants could grow on chalk. Many of the original plants were collected in China and the Himalayas.

Times Open all year: Apr-Sep, Mon-Fri 10-6. Winter: Oct-Nov & Feb-Mar, Mon-Fri, 10-4.30; Dec-Jan, 10-4. Facilities 🅿 🎌 (outdoor) ♿ (partly accessible) (gardens on a sloping site, may prove difficult for wheelchair users) toilets for disabled ⊗

GATESHEAD

Baltic Centre for Contemporary Art

South Shore Rd, Gateshead Quays NE8 3BA

☎ 0191 478 1810 & 440 4944

🖹 0191 478 1922

e-mail: info@balticmill.com

web: www.balticmill.com

dir: follow signs for Quayside, Millennium Bridge. 15 mins' walk from Gateshead Metro & Newcastle Central Station

Once a 1950s grain warehouse, part of the old Baltic Flour Mills, Baltic Centre for Contemporary Art is an international centre presenting a dynamic and ambitious programme of complementary exhibitions and events. It consists of five art spaces, cinema, auditorium, library and archive, eating and drinking areas and a shop. Check website for current events information.

Times Open all year daily 10-6 (Tue 10.30-6). Closed 25-26 Dec & 1 Jan. Facilities 🅿 🅿 🖵 🍴 licensed ♿ toilets for disabled shop ⊗

NEWCASTLE UPON TYNE

Discovery Museum

Blandford Square NE1 4JA
☎ 0191 232 6789 📠 0191 230 2614
e-mail: discovery@twmuseums.org.uk
web: www.twmuseums.org.uk/discovery
dir: off A6115/A6125. 5 mins walk from
Newcastle Central Station

Newcastle Discovery Museum offers something
for everyone. There are displays covering fashion,
military history, maritime splendours and
scientific curiosities. Local history is covered in
the fascinating Great City story. There is a gallery
housing Turbinia, once the world's fastest ship.

Times Open all year, Mon-Sat 10-5; Sun 2-5.
(Closed 25-26 Dec & 1 Jan). Facilities ℗ ⓟ ⌴
🚻 toilets for disabled shop ⊗

SUNDERLAND

Monkwearmouth Station Museum

North Bridge St SR5 1AP
☎ 0191 567 7075
dir: off A1018

Time stands still in this beautifully restored
Victorian station. Travel and transport in the
early 1900s are recorded with a look behind the
scenes of the booking offices and guard's van.
The brand new 'Play Station' activities area has
been specifically designed for young visitors with
regular organised events for children.

Times Open all year, Mon-Sat 10-5, Sun 2-5.
Closed 25-26 Dec & 1 Jan* Facilities ℗ 🚻
(partly accessible) toilets for disabled shop ⊗

SUNDERLAND

National Glass Centre

Liberty Way SR6 0GL
☎ 0191 515 5555 📄 0191 515 5556
e-mail: info@nationalglasscentre.com
web: www.nationalglasscentre.com
dir: A19 onto A1231, signposted from all major roads

The National Glass Centre offers galleries showing an international programme of exhibitions. Home to the largest art glass making facility for kiln forming, a unique venue and a hub for activity inspired by glass. Artists' studios, glass production facilities and much more and located in an innovative glass and steel building on the banks of the River Wear. Explore with a behind-the-scenes tours.

Times Open all year, daily 10-5 (last admission to glass tour 4.30). Closed 25 Dec & 1 Jan.
Facilities ℗ 🚻 🍴 licensed ♿ toilets for disabled shop ⊗

SUNDERLAND

Sunderland Museum & Winter Gardens

Burdon Rd SR1 1PP
☎ 0191 553 2323 📄 0191 553 7828
e-mail: sunderland@twmuseums.org.uk
web: www.twmuseums.org.uk/sunderland
dir: in city centre on Burdon Rd, short walk from Sunderland metro and mainline stations

An award-winning attraction with wide-ranging displays and many hands-on exhibits that cover the archaeology and geology of Sunderland, the coal mines and shipyards of the area and the spectacular glass and pottery made on Wearside. Other galleries show the changes in the lifestyles of Sunderland women over the past century, works by LS Lowry and wildlife from all corners of the globe. The Winter Gardens are a horticultural wonderland where the exotic plants from around the world can be seen growing to their full natural height in a spectacular glass and steel rotunda.

Times Open all year, Mon-Sat 10-5, Sun 2-5.*
Facilities ℗ 🚻 🍴 licensed ♿ toilets for disabled shop ⊗

RUGBY

The Webb Ellis Rugby Football Museum

5 Saint Matthew's St CV21 3BY
☎ 01788 567777   🖹 01788 537400
e-mail: sales@webb-ellis.co.uk
web: www.webb-ellis.co.uk
dir: on A428 opposite Rugby School

An intriguing collection of Rugby football memorabilia is housed in the shop in which rugby balls have been made since 1842. Visitors can watch a craftsman at work, hand-stitching the footballs. Situated near to Rugby School and its famous playing field.

Times Open all year, Mon-Sat 9-5. Phone for holiday opening times.* Facilities ℗ ⅊ (partly accessible) shop ⊗

STRATFORD-UPON-AVON

Royal Shakespeare Company Collection

Royal Shakespeare Theatre, Waterside
CV37 6BB
☎ 01789 262870   🖹 01789 262870
e-mail: info@rsc.org.uk
web: www.rsc.org.uk
dir: M40 junct 14 take A46 S. At 1st rdbt take 2nd exit (A439). At next rdbt follow signs to park & ride. In town centre follow RSC signs

The RSC gallery opened in 1881, and was part of the first Shakespeare Memorial Theatre. In 1926 fire destroyed the theatre leaving only a semi circular wall and the gallery. The rebuilt theatre was opened in 1932. In 2007 the theatre, known as the Royal Shakespeare Theatre since 1961, was closed for redevelopment work. It is due to re-open in 2010.

Times Closed for redevelopment in 2009. Due to open in 2010, please contact 01789 262870 for more details* Facilities ℗ ⅊ toilets for disabled shop ⊗

BIRMINGHAM

Aston Hall

Trinity Rd, Aston B6 6JD
☎ 0121 464 2193 📄 0121 327 7162
e-mail: bmag-enquiries@birmingham.gov.uk
web: www.bmag.org.uk
dir: E of Birmingham, just off the A4040 in
Yardley

Built by Sir Thomas Holte, Aston Hall is a fine
Jacobean mansion complete with a panelled Long
Gallery, balustraded staircase and magnificent
plaster friezes and ceilings. King Charles I spent
a night here during the Civil War and the house
was damaged by Parliamentary troops. It was
also leased to James Watt Junior, the son of the
great industrial pioneer.

Times Open Etr-Oct, Tue-Sun 11.30-4. Closed
Mon ex BHs.* Facilities 🅿 ⬛ ♿ (partly
accessible) shop ⊗

BIRMINGHAM

Birmingham Museum & Art Gallery

Chamberlain Sq B3 3DH
☎ 0121 303 2834 📄 0121 303 1394
e-mail: bmag-enquiries@birmingham.gov.uk
web: www.bmag.org.uk
dir: 5 mins walk from Birmingham New St
Station, by Town Hall, Council House & Central
Library

One of the world's best collections of Pre-
Raphaelite paintings can be seen here, including
important works by Burne-Jones, a native of
Birmingham. Also on display are fine silver,
ceramics and glass. The archaeology section
has prehistoric Egyptian, Greek and Roman
antiquities, and also objects from the Near
East, Mexico and Peru. New galleries explore
the creation of art, while the In Touch gallery
includes talking sculptures, and Samurai armour.
The Bull Ring explores the 800 year history of this
well-known area. There is a regular programme of
temporary art and history exhibitions every year.

Times Open all year, Mon-Thu & Sat 10-5, Fri
10.30-5 and Sun 12.30-5. Fees Admission
free but small charge may be made for some
temporary exhibitions Facilities 🅿 ⬛🍽
licensed ♿ toilets for disabled shop ⊗

BIRMINGHAM

Blakesley Hall

Blakesley Rd, Yardley B25 8RN
☎ 0121 464 2193 ▤ 0121 464 0400
e-mail: laura_r_cox@birmingham.gov.uk
web: www.bmag.org.uk
dir: A4040 onto Blakesley Rd, Hall 100yds on
right

Blakesley Hall is a fine Yeoman farmer's
residence, built by Richard Smalbroke in 1590. It
has a half-timbered exterior and a Stuart interior,
with a wonderful herb garden. The visitor centre
has a varied exhibition programme, tea room and
gift shop. Regular weekend events take place
throughout the open season.

Times Open Apr-Oct, Tue-Sun & BHs, 12-4*
Facilities ℗ ⌴ 🗔 (outdoor) ♿ (partly
accessible) toilets for disabled shop ⊗

BIRMINGHAM

Museum of the Jewellery Quarter

75-80 Vyse St, Hockley B18 6HA
☎ 0121 554 3598 ▤ 0121 554 9700
e-mail: bmag-enquiries@birmingham.gov.uk
web: www.bmag.org.uk
dir: off A41 into Vyse St, museum on left after
1st side street

The Museum tells the story of jewellery making in
Birmingham from its origins in the Middle Ages
right through to the present day. Discover the
skill of the jeweller's craft and enjoy a unique
tour of an original jewellery factory frozen in time.
For over eighty years the family firm of Smith
and Pepper produced jewellery from the factory.
This perfectly preserved 'time capsule' workshop
has changed little since the beginning of the
20th century. The Jewellery Quarter is still very
much at the forefront of jewellery manufacture in
Britain and the Museum showcases the work of
the city's most exciting new designers.

Times Open all year* Facilities ℗ ♿ toilets for
disabled shop ⊗

BIRMINGHAM

RSPB Sandwell Valley Nature Reserve

20 Tanhouse Av, Great Barr B43 5AG
☎ 0121 357 7395   ▤ 0121 358 3013
e-mail: sandwellvalley@rspb.org.uk
web: www.rspb.org.uk
dir: off B4167 Hamstead Rd into Tanhouse Ave

Opened in 1983 on the site of an old colliery, Sandwell Valley is home to hundreds of bird, animal and insect species in five different habitats. Summer is the best time to see the yellow wagtail or reed warblers, while wintertime attracts goosanders, snipe, and redshanks. There are guided walks and bug hunts for the kids in summer, and a shop and visitor centre all year round.

Times Open Tue-Fri 9-5, Sat & Sun 10-5 (closes at dusk in winter). Closed Mon, 24 Dec-2 Jan* Facilities ❷ ⓟ 🎋 (outdoor) ♿ (partly accessible) toilets for disabled shop

BIRMINGHAM

Sarehole Mill

Cole Bank Rd, Hall Green B13 0BD
☎ 0121 777 6612   ▤ 0121 303 2891
e-mail: bmag-enquiries@birmingham.gov.uk
web: www.bmag.org.uk
dir: A34 towards Birmingham. After 5m turn left on B4146, attraction on left

Sarehole Mill was built in the 1760s. Used for both flour production and metal rolling up to the last century, the Mill can still be seen in action first Sunday each month during the summer months. Restored with financial backing from JRR Tolkien, who grew up in the area and cites Sarehole as an influence for writing The Hobbit and Lord of the Rings. Tolkein Weekend takes place during May each year.

Times Open Etr-Oct, Tue-Sun noon-4. (Closed Mon, ex BH Mon)* Facilities ❷ ⬛ ♿ (partly accessible) ⊗

BIRMINGHAM

Soho House

Soho Av, Handsworth B18 5LB
☎ 0121 554 9122 📄 0121 554 5929
e-mail: bmag-enquiries@birmingham.gov.uk
web: www.bmag.org.uk
dir: from city centre follow A41 to Soho Rd, follow
brown heritage signs to Soho Ave

Soho House was the elegant home of industrial
pioneer Matthew Boulton between 1766 and
1809. Here, he met with some of the most
important thinkers and scientists of his day. The
house has been carefully restored and contains
many of Boulton's possessions including
furniture, clocks, silverware and the original
dining table where the Lunar Society met.

Times Open Etr-Oct, Tue-Sun 12-4. (Closed Mon
ex BH Mons)* Facilities ℗ 💻 🎪 ♿ toilets for
disabled shop ⊗

COVENTRY

Coventry Transport Museum

Millennium Place, Hales St CV1 1JD
☎ 024 7623 4270 📄 024 7623 4284
e-mail: enquiries@transport-museum.com
web: www.transport-museum.com
dir: just off junct 1, Coventry ring road, Tower St
in city centre

Coventry is the traditional home of the British
motor industry, and the museum's world-
renowned collection displays over 150 years of its
history. You can design your own car, feel what
its like to break the sound barrier at 763mph
and even travel into the future. The Festival of
Motoring takes place over the fist weekend in
September and features vintage, veteran and
classic vehicles with family activities and stunt
show riders culminating in a car and motorcycle
rally around the region.

Times Open all year, daily 10-5. Closed 24-26
Dec & 1 Jan Facilities ℗ 💻 ♿ toilets for
disabled shop ⊗

COVENTRY

Herbert Art Gallery & Museum

Jordan Well CV1 5QP
☎ 024 7683 2386
e-mail: info@theherbert.org
web: www.theherbert.org
dir: in city centre near Cathedral

The Herbert Art and Gallery Museum, located next to Coventry Cathedral, has undergone a £20 million redevelopment. The site has eight permanent galleries, history centre and media suites. There is also an active programme of temporary exhibitions, and plenty of events and activities for children. Please contact for details of forthcoming events. The Museum will celebrate its 50th Anniversary in 2010.

Times Open all year, Mon-Sat 10-5.30, Sun 12-5. Closed 24-26, 31 Dec & 1 Jan.* Facilities ℗ ☕ ♿ toilets for disabled shop ⊗

COVENTRY

Jaguar Daimler Heritage Centre

Browns Ln, Allesley CV5 9DR
☎ 024 7620 3322 🖹 024 7620 2835
e-mail: jagtrust@jaguar.com
web: www.jdht.com
dir: on A45, follow signs for Browns Lane Plant

Established in 1983, the Jaguar-Daimler Heritage Trust maintains a unique collection of motor vehicles and artefacts manufactured by Jaguar Cars Ltd, and the many other renowned marques associated with the company.

Times Open wkdays by appointment, no appointment required on last Sun of mth.* Facilities ℗ ☕ toilets for disabled shop ⊗

COVENTRY

Priory Visitor Centre

Priory Row CV1 5EX

☎ 024 7655 2242 📄 024 7622 0171

e-mail: prioryvisitorscentre@coventry.gov.uk

web: www.theherbert.org

dir: in city centre near Cathedral

Earl Leofric and his wife Lady Godiva founded a monastery in Coventry in the 11th century. This priory disappeared somewhere beneath the cathedral that was built on the site, until this cathedral was in turn demolished by Henry VIII in the 16th century. Soon after that most of the buildings on the site had been reduced to ground level, leaving modern archaeologists to discover the outlines of history. This visitor centre displays finds from the site as well as telling the story of Coventry's first cathedral.

Times Open Mon-Sat 10-5.30, Sun noon-4*
Facilities ℗ toilets for disabled shop ⊗

COVENTRY

St Mary's Guildhall

Bayley Ln CV1 5RN

☎ 024 7683 3328 📄 024 7683 3329

e-mail: mark.twissell@coventry.gov.uk

web: www.coventry.gov.uk/stmarys

dir: in city centre near Herbert Art Gallery & south side of old Cathedral ruins

This impressive medieval Guildhall has stood in the heart of Coventry for over 650 years, and has played its part in the history of the area. It served as Henry VI's court during the War of the Roses, was a prison to Mary Queen of Scots, and was used as a setting by George Eliot in her novel Adam Bede. The Great Hall contains a Tournai tapestry commissioned for the visit of Henry VII and Queen Elizabeth in 1500.

Times Open Mar-Oct, Sun-Thu 10-4 Facilities ℗
🍴 licensed ♿ (partly accessible) toilets for disabled shop ⊗

DUDLEY

Museum & Art Gallery

St James's Rd DY1 1HU
☎ 01384 815575 🖷 01384 815576
e-mail: dudley.museum@dudley.gov.uk
web: www.dudley.gov.uk
dir: M5 N junct 2. Take A4123 signed to Dudley

The museum houses the Brooke Robinson collection of 17th-, 18th- and 19th-century European painting, furniture, ceramics and enamels. A fine geological gallery, 'The Time Trail' has spectacular displays of fossils from the local Wenlock limestone and coal measures. A changing programme of exhibitions including the new Saxons and Vikings exhibition, permanent Duncan Edwards and Local Heroes exhibition.

Times Open all year, Mon-Sat 10-4. Closed BHs & Good Fri. Facilities ℗ ₺ toilets for disabled shop ⊗

KINGSWINFORD

Broadfield House Glass Museum

Compton Dr DY6 9NS
☎ 01384 812745
e-mail: glass.museum@dudley.gov.uk
web: www.glassmuseum.org.uk
dir: Off A491 Stourbridge to Wolverhampton road, just S of Kingswinford Village Centre, follow brown tourist signs

Situated in the historic Stourbridge Glass Quarter, Broadfield House Glass Museum is one of the best glass museums in the world. Home to a magnificent collection of British glass from the 17th century to the present day, the museum hosts an exciting programme of exhibitions and events, and is a main venue for the International Festival of Glass, which is held bi-ennially. The museum also has a gift shop, and a hot glass studio. April 2010 marks the 30th anniversary of the opening of the museum.

Times Open all year, Tue-Sun 12-4. Please phone for Xmas & Etr openings.* Facilities ℗ ₺ (partly accessible) (access restricted to ground floor, studio & temporary exhibitions) toilets for disabled shop ⊗

WALSALL

The New Art Gallery Walsall

Gallery Square WS2 8LG
☎ 01922 654400 📄 01922 654401
e-mail: info@artatwalsall.org.uk
web: www.artatwalsall.org.uk
dir: signed from all major routes into town centre

Opened in 2000, this exciting new art gallery has at its core the Garman Ryan Collection, and a Children's Discovery Gallery that offers access to the very best in contemporary art in the only interactive art gallery designed especially for young people.

Times Open all year, Tue-Sat 10-5, Sun noon-5. Closed Mon ex BH Mon, 25-28 Dec & 1 Jan. Please telephone to confirm.* Facilities ℗ 🆒 ♿ toilets for disabled shop ⊗

WALSALL

Walsall Leather Museum

Littleton Street West WS2 8EQ
☎ 01922 721153 📄 01922 725827
e-mail: leathermuseum@walsall.gov.uk
web: www.walsall.gov.uk/leathermuseum
dir: On Walsall ring-road A4148 on N side of town

Award winning working museum in the saddlery and leathergoods 'capital' of Britain. Watch skilled craftsmen and women at work in this restored Victorian leather factory. Displays tell the story of Walsall's leatherworkers past and present. Large shop stocks range of Walsall-made leathergoods, many at bargain prices. Groups very welcome, guided tours available.

Times Open all year, Tue-Sat 10-5 (Nov-Mar 4). Closed Sun-Mon. Open BH Mon. Closed 24-26 Dec, 1 Jan, Good Fri, Etr Sun & May Day. Facilities ℗ 🆒 🅰 (outdoor) ♿ toilets for disabled shop ⊗

WOLVERHAMPTON

Bantock House and Park

Finchfield Rd WV3 9LQ

☎ 01902 552195 📄 01902 552196
e-mail: bantockhouse@wolverhampton.gov.uk
web: www.wolverhamptonart.org.uk
dir: follow signs for Wolverhampton. Bantock House 1m out of city & well signed from ring road

A restored Georgian farmhouse set within 43 acres and surrounded by beautiful formal gardens. Visitors can explore the period settings of the Bantock's former home and discover stories about the family and other Victorians that helped to shape Wolverhampton. The house has permanent displays of exquisite locally made japanned-ware, enamels and steel jewellery, as well as a programme of changing exhibitions. Picnic areas, children's playground and pitch and putt. Please telephone or email for a quarterly events leaflet.

Times Open all year, Apr-end Oct, 11-5; Nov-end Mar, 12-4. Closed Mon except BH* Facilities ℗ ⊡ 🎋 (outdoor) ♿ toilets for disabled shop ⊗

WORDSLEY

The Red House Glass Cone

High St DY8 4AZ

☎ 01384 812750 📄 01384 812751
e-mail: redhouse.cone@dudley.gov.uk
web: www.redhousecone.co.uk
dir: A491 just N of Stourbridge

One of only four cones left in the UK and one of the most complete glass cone sites in Europe, over one hundred feet tall, Red House was built in the 18th century. The cone was in use until 1936, and housed a furnace around which men blew glass. This is a busy heritage site hosting exhibitions, events, children's activities, tours, a schools' programme, live glass-making and craft studios. International Festival of Glass is being held 27-30 August 2010.

Times Open all year, daily, 10-4. Please check for Xmas opening times.* Facilities ℗ ⊡ 🎋 (outdoor) ♿ (partly accessible) toilets for disabled shop ⊗

BRIGHSTONE

Brighstone Shop and Museum

North St PO30 4AX

☎ 01983 740689 📄 01983 740689

e-mail: isleofwight@nationaltrust.org.uk

web: www.nationaltrust.org.uk/isleofwight

dir: off B3399 in Brighstone into North Street, next to Post Office

Situated within a row of attractive, thatched cottages you will find this museum which contains an evocative tableau and an interesting exhibition on village life in the 19th century, and the National Trust shop.

Times Open all year, Mon-Sat; 2 Jan-1 Apr 10-1; 2 Apr-28 May & 27 Sep-24 Dec10-4; 29 May-25 Sep 10-5. Open Sun 30 May-26 Sep 12-5. Facilities ⓟ ᵔ shop ⊗ ⫯

BRADFORD-ON-AVON

Bradford-on-Avon Tithe Barn

web: www.english-heritage.org.uk

dir: 0.25m S of town centre, off B3109

This impressive tithe barn, over 160ft long by 30ft wide, once belonged to Shaftesbury Abbey. The roof is of stone slates, supported outside by buttresses and inside by massive beams and a network of rafters.

Times Open all year, daily 10.30-4. Closed 25 Dec.* Facilities ⓟ ⊗ ⫯

LUDGERSHALL

Ludgershall Castle and Cross

SP11 9QR
web: www.english-heritage.org.uk
dir: 7m NW of Andover on A342

Ruins of an early 12th-century royal hunting palace and medieval cross. The visitor can see large earthworks of the Norman motte-and-bailey castle and the flint walls of the later hunting palace. The stump of a medieval cross stands in the village street.

Times Open at any reasonable time.*
Facilities ℗ ♯

WOODHENGE

Woodhenge

web: www.english-heritage.org.uk
dir: 1.5m N of Amesbury, off A345 just S of Durrington

A Neolithic ceremonial monument dating from about 2300 BC, consisting of six concentric rings of timber posts, now marked by concrete piles. The long axis of the rings, which are oval, points to the rising sun on Midsummer Day.

Times Open any reasonable time. (Usual facilities may not apply around Summer Solstice 20-22 Jun. Please check).* Facilities ℗ ♯

WORCESTER

City Museum & Art Gallery

Foregate St WR1 1DT
☎ 01905 25371 📄 01905 616979
e-mail:
artgalleryandmuseum@cityofworcester.gov.uk
web: www.worcestercitymuseums.org.uk
dir: in city centre, 150m from Foregate St Train
Station

The gallery has temporary art exhibitions from
both local and national sources. Museum exhibits
cover geology, local and natural history. There
are collections relating to the Worcestershire
Regiment and the Worcestershire Yeomanry
Cavalry.

Times Open all year, Tue-Sat 10.30-4.30, Sat
9.30-5. Closed Sun, 25-26 Dec, 1 Jan & Good Fri,
Easter Mon and Whitsun BH Mon.* Facilities ℗
🖵 ♿ toilets for disabled shop ⊗

BURTON AGNES

Burton Agnes Manor House

web: www.english-heritage.org.uk
dir: in Burton Agnes, 5m SW of Bridlington on
A166

A rare and well-preserved example of a Norman
house. Some interesting Norman architectural
features can still be seen, but the building
was encased in brick during the 17th and 18th
centuries. The house is near Burton Agnes Hall
and the gardens are privately owned and not
managed by English Heritage.

Times Open 21 Mar-Oct, daily 11-5.*
Facilities ⊞

KINGSTON UPON HULL

`Streetlife' - Hull Museum of Transport

High St HU1 1PS

☎ 01482 613902 📄 01482 613710

e-mail: museums@hullcc.gov.uk

web: www.hullcc.gov.uk

dir: A63 from M62, follow signs for Old Town

This purpose-built museum uses a 'hands-on' approach to trace 200 years of transport history. With a vehicle collection of national importance, state-of-the-art animatronic displays and authentic scenarios, you can see Hull's Old Town brought vividly to life. The mail coach ride uses the very latest in computer technology to recreate a Victorian journey by four-in-hand.

Times Open all year, Mon-Sat 10-5, Sun 1.30-4.30. Closed 24-25 Dec & Good Fri*

Facilities ℗ ⊨ ᕕ toilets for disabled shop ⊗

KINGSTON UPON HULL

Maister House

160 High St HU1 1NL

☎ 01482 324114 📄 01482 227003

web: www.nationaltrust.org.uk

dir: Hull city centre

The house is a mid-18th-century rebuilding, notable for its splendid stone and wrought-iron staircase, ornate stucco work and finely carved doors. Only the staircase and entrance hall are open as the house is now let as offices.

Times Open all year, Mon-Fri 10-4 (Closed BH).*

Facilities ℗ ᕕ (partly accessible) ⊗ ⍦ ⅍

KINGSTON UPON HULL

Maritime Museum

Queen Victoria Square HU1 3DX
☎ 01482 613902 📄 01482 613710
e-mail: museums@hullcc.gov.uk
web: www.hullcc.gov.uk
dir: A63 to town centre, museum is within
pedestrian area

Hull's maritime history is illustrated here, with
displays on whales and whaling, ships and
shipping, and other aspects of this Humber port.
There is also a Victorian court room which is used
for temporary exhibitions. The restored dock area,
with its fine Victorian and Georgian buildings, is
well worth exploring too.

Times Open all year, Mon-Sat 10-5 & Sun
1.30-4.30. Closed 25 Dec-2 Jan & Good Fri*
Facilities ℗ ♿ (partly accessible) shop ⊗

KINGSTON UPON HULL

Wilberforce House

23-25 High St HU1 1NE
☎ 01482 613902 📄 01482 613710
e-mail: museums@hullcc.gov.uk
web: www.hullcc.gov.uk
dir: A63 from M62 or A1079 from York, follow
signs for Old Town

The early 17th-century Merchant's house was the
birthplace of William Wilberforce, who became a
leading campaigner against slavery. Re-opened
in 2007 after full refurbishment the House tells
the story of slavery, abolition, the triangular trade
and explores modern issues surrounding slavery.

Times Open all year, Mon-Sat 10-5 & Sun
1.30-4.30. Closed 25-26 Dec, 1 Jan & Good Fri.*
Facilities ℗ 🏕 (outdoor) ♿ shop ⊗

EASBY

Easby Abbey

web: www.english-heritage.org.uk
dir: 1m SE of Richmond off B6271

Set beside the River Swale, this Premonstratensian Abbey was founded in 1155 and dedicated to St Agatha. Extensive remains of the monks' domestic buildings can be seen.

Times Open all year, 21 Mar-Sep, daily 10-6; Oct, daily 10-5; Nov-Mar, daily 10-4. Closed 24-26 Dec & 1 Jan* Facilities ℗ ⊞

GRASSINGTON

National Park Centre

Hebden Rd BD23 5LB
☎ 01969 751690   📄 01756 751699
e-mail: grassington@yorkshiredales.org.uk
web: www.yorkshiredales.org.uk
dir: situated on B6265 in the main Grassington car park

The centre is a useful introduction to the Yorkshire Dales National Park. Maps, guides and local information are available. There is also a 24-hr public access information service and a full tourist information service. The centre has recently been refurbished with the emphasis on agriculture and climate change. A video display explains this.

Times Open all year, Apr-Oct daily, 10-5; Nov-Mar, Fri, & Sat-Sun, 10-4 (also daily in school hols). Closed Jan 2010. Facilities ℗ ⊓ ♿ toilets for disabled shop

MALHAM

Malham National Park Centre

BD23 4DA

☎ 01969 652380 📠 01969 652389

e-mail: malham@yorkshiredales.org.uk

web: www.yorkshiredales.org.uk

dir: off A65 at Gargrave opposite petrol station. Malham 7m

The Yorkshire Dales National Park centre has maps, guides and local information together with displays on the remarkable natural history of the area and work of conservation bodies.

Times Open, Apr-Oct, daily 10-5; Winter, Sat-Sun, 10-4. Daily in school hols. Closed Jan.* Facilities ℗ ⴰ (outdoor) ⴳ toilets for disabled shop

MIDDLESBROUGH

Captain Cook Birthplace Museum

Stewart Park, Marton TS7 8AT

☎ 01642 311211 📠 01642 515659

e-mail: captcookmuseum@middlesbrough.gov.uk

web: www.captcook-ne.co.uk

dir: 3m S on A172

Opened to mark the 250th anniversary of the birth of the voyager in 1728, this museum illustrates the early life of James Cook and his discoveries with permanent and temporary exhibitions. Located in spacious and rolling parkland, the site also offers outside attractions for the visitor. The museum has a special resource centre which has fresh approaches to presentation with computers, films, special effects, interactives and educational aids.

Times Open all year: Mar-Oct, Tue-Sun, 10-5.30. Nov-Feb 9-4.00. (Last entry 45 mins before closure). Closed Mon & some BH, 24-26 Dec,1 Jan & 1st full week Jan.* Facilities ℗ ℗ ⌷ ⵣ licensed ⴰ (outdoor) ⴳ toilets for disabled shop ⊗

REDCAR

RNLI Zetland Museum

5 King St TS10 3DT
☎ 01642 494311 & 471813
e-mail: zetland.museum@yahoo.co.uk
dir: on corner of King St and The Promenade

The museum portrays the lifeboat, maritime, fishing and local history of the area, including its main exhibit The Zetland, the oldest lifeboat in the world, dating from 1802. There is also a replica of a fisherman's cottage c1900 and almost 2000 other exhibits. The museum is housed in an early lifeboat station, now a listed building.

Times Open May, Wed 11-4, Sat-Sun 12-4; Jun-Sep, Tue-Fri 11-4, Sat-Sun 12-4. Closed Mon.*
Facilities ℗ ⧗ (partly accessible) shop

WINTRINGHAM

Wolds Way Lavender

Deer Farm Park, Sandy Ln, Wintringham
YO17 8HW
☎ 01944 758641 📄 01944 758641
e-mail: admin@woldswaylavender.co.uk
web: www.woldswaylavender.co.uk
dir: off A64 between Malton & Scarborough, follow brown signs

The medicinal and therapeutic benefits of lavender are extolled at this 12-acre site close to the Yorkshire Wolds. Four acres are currently planted with lavender, and there is a wood-burning still for the extraction of lavender oil. Visitors can be calmed by the Sensory Areas, enjoy a cuppa in the tearoom, and purchase all manner of lavender items at the farm shop.

Times Open Apr-Oct, Sun-Thu (closed Fri-Sat); Jun-Aug daily 10-5. Facilities ℗ ⧗ 🪑 (outdoor) ⧗ toilets for disabled shop ⊗

YORK

Guildhall

Coney St YO1 9QN

☎ 01904 613161 📄 01904 551052

web: www.york.gov.uk

dir: 5-10mins walk from rail station

The present Hall dates from 1446 but in 1942 an air raid virtually destroyed the building. The present Guildhall was carefully restored as an exact replica and was re-opened in 1960. There is an interesting arch-braced roof decorated with colourful bosses and supported by 12 solid oak pillars. There are also some beautiful stained-glass windows.

Times Open all year, May-Oct, Mon-Fri 9-5, Sat 10-5, Sun 2-5; Nov-Apr, Mon-Fri 9-5.*
Facilities ℗ ♿ toilets for disabled ⊗ �

YORK

National Railway Museum

Leeman Rd YO26 4XJ

☎ 01904 621261 📄 01904 611112

e-mail: nrm@nrm.org.uk

web: www.nrm.org.uk

dir: behind rail station. Signed from all major roads and city centre

The National Railway Museum is the world's largest railway museum. From record breakers to history makers the museum is home to a vast collection of locomotives, carriages and wagons, including The Royal Trains, a replica of Stephenson's Rocket, the Japanese Bullet Train and the elegant Duchess. With three enormous galleries, interactive exhibits and daily events, the National Railway Museum mixes education with fun. This attraction is also free. NB: There is a charge for certain special events.

Times Open all year 10-6. Closed 24-26 Dec.
Fees Admission is free but there may be charges for special events and rides. Facilities ℗ ℗ 🖵 ⑪ licensed 🛏 (outdoor) ♿ toilets for disabled shop ⊗

York City Art Gallery

Exhibition Square YO1 7EW
☎ 01904 687687   📠 01904 697966
web: www.york.trust.museum
dir: 3 min walk from The Minster in city centre

The gallery is remarkable for the range and
quality of its collections that provide a survey
of most developments in Western European
painting over the past six centuries. Works by
Parmigianino, Bellotto, Lely, Reynolds, Frith,
Boudin, Lowry and Nash are on permanent
display. There are also fine collections of
watercolours and pottery.

Times Open all year, daily 10-5. (Closed 25-26
Dec & 1 Jan). Facilities ℗ 🖵 🎠 (indoor) ♿
toilets for disabled shop ⊗

Cusworth Hall, Museum and Park Hall

Cusworth Ln DN5 7TU
☎ 01302 782342   📠 01302 800040
e-mail: museum@doncaster.gov.uk
web: www.doncaster.gov.uk
dir: 3m NW of Doncaster off A638. Signed

Cusworth Hall is an 18th-century country house
set in a landscaped park. It has displays which
illustrate the way local people here lived, worked
and entertained themselves over the last 200
years. The Hall and Park have recently reopened
following extensive refurbishment, giving visitors
access to the magnificent Chapel and Great
Kitchen. The Park features a pleasure grounds,
18th-century lake system, lawns and woodland.
The Tea Room is noted for its homemade food.

Times Open all year, Mon-Fri 10.30-5, Sat-Sun
1-5. Park open 24hrs.* Facilities ℗ 🖵 ♿ toilets
for disabled shop ⊗

DONCASTER

Doncaster Museum & Art Gallery

Chequer Rd DN1 2AE

☎ 01302 734293 📠 01302 735409

e-mail: museum@doncaster.gov.uk

web: www.doncaster.gov.uk/museums

dir: off inner ring road

The wide-ranging collections include fine and decorative art and sculpture. Also ceramics, glass, silver, and displays on history, archaeology and natural history. The historical collection of the Kings Own Yorkshire Light Infantry is housed here. A recent addition is the 'By River and Road' gallery, which details the history of the Doncaster area. Temporary exhibitions are held.

Times Open all year, Mon-Sat 10-5, Sun 2-5. (Closed Good Fri, 25-26 Dec & 1 Jan).*

Facilities 🅿 🅿 ♿ toilets for disabled shop ⊗

SHEFFIELD

Abbeydale Industrial Hamlet

Abbeydale Industrial Hamlet, Abbeydale Road South S7 2QW

☎ 0114 236 7731

e-mail: postmaster@simt.co.uk

web: www.simt.co.uk

dir: Turn off A61 south, follow A621 Abbeydale road to Abbeydale Road South towards Bakewell

Worker's houses, water wheels, crucible steel, furnaces, tilt hammers and workshops create a unique atmosphere of life at home and at work in a scythe and steel works, dating back to the 18th century. The works gallery tells the story of one of the largest water powered industrial complex, on Sheffield's River Sheaf. Look out for Abbeydale family Sunday events.

Times Open Apr-Oct. Open all year for pre-booked school and group visits. Facilities 🅿 🅿 ⊑ ♿ (partly accessible) shop ⊗

SHEFFIELD

Millennium Gallery

Arundel Gate S1 2PP
☎ 0114 278 2600 📄 0114 278 2604
e-mail: info@museums-sheffield.org.uk
web: www.museums-sheffield.org.uk
dir: Follow signs to city centre, then follow the
brown signs marked M).

With four different galleries under one roof, the
Millennium Gallery has something for everyone.
Enjoy new blockbuster exhibitions drawn from
the collections of Britain's national galleries
and museums, including the Victoria & Albert
Museum and Tate Gallery. See the best of
contemporary craft and design in a range of
exhibitions by established and up-and-coming
makers. Be dazzled by Sheffield's magnificent
and internationally important collection of
decorative and domestic metalwork and
silverware. Discover the Ruskin Gallery with its
wonderful array of treasures by Victorian artist
and writer John Ruskin.

Times Open all year, daily Mon-Sat 10-5, Sun
11-5.* Fees Admission prices apply for some
special exhibitions (concessions available).
Facilities ℗ 🖵 🍴 licensed toilets for disabled
shop ⊗

BRADFORD

Bolling Hall

Bowling Hall Rd BD4 7LP
☎ 01274 431826 📄 01274 726220
web: www.bradfordmuseums.org
dir: 1m from city centre off A650

A classic West Yorkshire manor house, complete
with galleried 'housebody' (hall), Bolling Hall
dates mainly from the 17th century but has
medieval and 18th-century sections. It has
panelled rooms, plasterwork in original colours,
heraldic glass and a rare Chippendale bed.

Times Open all year, Wed-Fri 11-4, Sat 10-5, Sun
12-5. Closed Mon ex BH, Good Fri, 25-26 Dec.*
Facilities ℗ ℗ shop ⊗

BRADFORD

Bradford Industrial Museum and Horses at Work

Moorside Mills, Moorside Rd, Eccleshill BD2 3HP

☎ 01274 435900 📄 01274 636362
web: www.bradfordmuseums.org
dir: off A658

Moorside Mills is an original spinning mill, now part of a museum that brings vividly to life the story of Bradford's woollen industry. There is the machinery that once converted raw wool into cloth, and the mill yard rings with the sound of iron on stone as shire horses pull trams, haul buses and give rides. Daily demonstrations and changing exhibitions.

Times Open all year, Tue-Sat 10-5, Sun 12-5. Closed Mon ex BH, Good Fri & 25-26 Dec*
Facilities 🅿 ⬚ toilets for disabled shop ⊗

BRADFORD

Cartwright Hall Art Gallery

Lister Park BD9 4NS

☎ 01274 431212 📄 01274 481045
e-mail: cartwright.hall@bradford.gov.uk
web: www.bradfordmuseums.org
dir: 1m from city centre on A650

Built in dramatic Baroque style in 1904, the gallery has permanent collections of 19th and 20th-century British art, contemporary prints, and older works by British and European masters.

Times Open all year, Tue-Sat 10-5, Sun 1-5. Closed Mon ex BH, Good Fri & 25-26 Dec.*
Facilities 🅿 🅟 toilets for disabled shop ⊗

BRADFORD

National Media Museum

Pictureville BD1 1NQ

☎ 01274 202030 📠 01274 723155
e-mail: talk@nationalmediamuseum.org.uk
web: www.nationalmediamuseum.org.uk
dir: 2m from end of M606, follow signs for city centre

Journey through popular photography and visit IMAX - the world's powerful giant screen experience, discover the past, present and future of television in Experience TV, watch your favourite TV moments in TV Heaven, play with light, lenses and colour in the Magic Factory and explore the world of animation - watch a real animator at work in the Animation Gallery. There are also temporary exhibitions and various special events are planned, please see the website for details.

Times Open all year, Tue-Sun 10-6, BH Mon & school hols. Closed 24-26 Dec.* **Fees** Admission to permanent galleries free, IMAX Cinema £6.95 (concessions £4.95). DMR (Feature length films) £8 (£6 concesssions). Groups 20% discount.* **Facilities** 🅿 Ⓟ 🖵 🍴 licensed 🍴 (Indoor) ♿ toilets for disabled shop ⊗

GOMERSAL

Red House

Oxford Rd BD19 4JP

☎ 01274 335100 📠 01274 335105
web: www.kirkleesmc.gov.uk/community/
museums.museum.shtml
dir: M62 junct 26, take A58 towards Leeds then right onto A651 towards Gomersal. Red House on right

Delightful redbrick house displayed as the 1830s home of a Yorkshire wool clothier and merchant. The house and family was frequently visited by Charlotte Brontë in the 1830s and featured in her novel Shirley. The gardens have been reconstructed in the style of the period and there are exhibitions on the Brontë connection and local history in restored barn and cartsheds.

Times Open all year, Mon-Fri 11-5, Sat-Sun 12-5. Telephone for Xmas opening. Closed Good Fri & 1 Jan. **Facilities** 🅿 Ⓟ ♿ (partly accessible) (ground floor of Red House accessible) toilets for disabled shop ⊗

HALIFAX

Bankfield Museum

Boothtown Rd, Akroyd Park HX3 6HG

☎ 01422 354823 & 352334

📠 01422 349020

e-mail: bankfield-museum@calderdale.gov.uk

web: www.calderdale.gov.uk

dir: on A647 Bradford via Queensbury road, 0.5m from Halifax town centre

Built by Edward Akroyd in the 1860s, this Renaissance-style building is set in parkland on a hill overlooking the town. It has an outstanding collection of costumes and textiles from many periods and parts of the world, including a new gallery featuring East European textiles. There is also a section on toys, and the museum of the Duke of Wellington's Regiment is housed here. Temporary exhibitions are held and there is a lively programme of events, workshops and activities. Please ring for details.

Times Open all year, Tue-Sat 10-5, Sun 1-4, BH Mon 10-5.* Facilities ℗ ℗ ⅊ (partly accessible) toilets for disabled shop ⊗

HALIFAX

Halifax Visitor Centre and Art Gallery

HX1 1RE

☎ 01422 368725

e-mail: halifax@ytbtic.co.uk

web: www.calderdale.gov.uk

dir: follow brown tourist signs, close to railway station

The merchants of Halifax built the elegant and unique hall in 1770, and it has over 300 merchant's rooms around a courtyard, now housing an art gallery and visitor centre. There are around eight temporary exhibitions each year.

Times Open all year, daily 10-5. (Closed 1 Jan & 25-26 Dec).* Facilities ℗ 🅟 (outdoor) ⅊ toilets for disabled shop ⊗

HUDDERSFIELD

Tolson Memorial Museum

Ravensknowle Park, Wakefield Rd HD5 8DJ
☎ 01484 223830　📄 01484 223843
e-mail: tolson.museum@kirkdees.gov.uk
web: tolson.museum.co.uk
dir: on A629, 1m from town centre

Displays on the development of the cloth industry
and a collection of horse-drawn vehicles,
together with natural history, archaeology, toys
and folk exhibits. There is a full programme of
events and temporary exhibitions.

Times Open all year. Mon-Fri 11-5, Sat & Sun
noon-5. Closed Xmas.* Facilities 🅿 🅟 toilets
for disabled shop ⊗

ILKLEY

Manor House Gallery & Museum

Castle Yard, Church St LS29 9DT
☎ 01943 600066　📄 01943 817079
web: www.bradfordmuseums.org
dir: behind Ilkley Parish Church, on A65

This Elizabethan manor house, one of Ilkley's few
buildings to pre-date the 19th century, was built
on the site of a Roman fort. Part of the Roman
wall can be seen, together with Roman objects
and displays on archaeology. There is a collection
of 17th and 18th-century farmhouse parlour and
kitchen furniture, and the art gallery exhibits
works by contemporary artists and craftspeople.

Times Open all year, Tue-Sat 1-5, Sun 1-4.
Open BH Mon. Closed Good Fri, 25-28 Dec.*
Facilities 🅟 shop ⊗

141

KEIGHLEY

Cliffe Castle Museum & Gallery

Spring Gardens Ln BD20 6LH
☎ 01535 618230   📠 01535 610536
web: www.bradfordmuseums.org
dir: NW of town off A629

Built as a millionaire's mansion, the house displays Victorian interiors, together with collections of local and natural history, ceramics, dolls, geological items and minerals. There is a play area and aviary in the grounds. Temporary exhibitions throughout the year.

Times Open all year, Tue-Sat 10-5, Sun 12-5. Open BH Mon. Closed Good Fri & 25-28 Dec.* Facilities ℗ 🖵 ♿ (partly accessible) (upstairs galleries hard to access by disabled users) toilets for disabled shop ⊗

LEEDS

Kirkstall Abbey

Abbey Rd, Kirkstall LS5 3EH
☎ 0113 274 8041
e-mail: kirkstall.abbey@leeds.gov.uk
web: www.leeds.gov.uk
dir: off A65, W of city centre

The most complete 12th-century Cistercian Abbey in the country stands on the banks of the River Aire. Many of the original buildings can still be seen, including the cloister, church and refectory. Regular tours take visitors to areas not normally accessible to the public. During the summer the Abbey hosts plays, fairs and musical events. A new visitor centre gives an insight into the history of the Abbey and a true sense of how the monks lived in the 15th century.

Times Open all year, abbey site open dawn to dusk. Visitor centre open: Tue-Thu 10-4, Sat-Sun 10-4. Open BHs.* Facilities ℗ Ⓟ 🪑 (outdoor) ♿ toilets for disabled shop

LEEDS

Leeds Art Gallery

The Headrow LS1 3AA
☎ 0113 247 8256 📄 0113 244 9689
e-mail: city.art.gallery@leeds.gov.uk
web: www.leeds.gov.uk/artgallery
dir: in city centre, next to town hall and library

Leeds Art Gallery has something to offer everyone. Home to one of the best collections of 20th-century British art outside London, as well as Victorian and late 19th-century pictures, an outstanding collection of English watercolours, a display of modern sculpture and temporary exhibitions focusing on contemporary art. The gallery holds an active events programme with talks, demonstrations and workshops regularly planned. Wander through the newly-opened Victorian Tiled Hall to access Leeds Central Library.

Times Open all year, Mon-Tue 10-8, Wed 12-8, Thu-Sat 10-5, Sun 1-5. Closed BHs.*
Facilities ⓟ 🏧 🍴 licensed ♿ (partly accessible) (restricted access to upper floor) toilets for disabled shop ⊗

LEEDS

Royal Armouries Museum

Armouries Dr LS10 1LT
☎ 0113 220 1999 & 0990 106 666
📄 0113 220 1955
e-mail: enquiries@armouries.org.uk
web: www.royalarmouries.org
dir: off A61 close to Leeds centre, follow brown heritage signs.

The museum is an impressive contemporary home for the renowned national collection of arms and armour. The collection is divided between five galleries: War, Tournament, Self-Defence, Hunting and Oriental. The Hall of Steel features a 100ft-high mass of 3000 pieces of arms and armour. Visitors are encouraged to take part in and handle some of the collections. Live demonstrations and interpretations take place throughout the year.

Times Open all year, daily, from 10-5. Closed 24-25 Dec* Facilities ⓟ 🏧 🍴 licensed 🪑 (indoor) toilets for disabled shop ⊗

143

MIDDLESTOWN

National Coal Mining Museum for England

Caphouse Colliery, New Rd WF4 4RH
☎ 01924 848806 📠 01924 844567
e-mail: info@ncm.org.uk
web: www.ncm.org.uk
dir: on A642 between Huddersfield & Wakefield

A unique opportunity to go 140 metres underground down one of Britain's oldest working mines. Take a step back in time with one of the museum's experienced local miners who will guide parties around the underground workings, where models and machinery depict methods and conditions of mining from the early 1800s to present day. Other attractions include the Hope Pit, pithead baths, Victorian steam winder, nature trail and adventure playground and meet the last ever working pit ponies. You are strongly advised to wear sensible footwear and warm clothing.

Times Open all year, daily 10-5. Closed 24-26 Dec & 1 Jan.* Facilities 🅿 ☕ 🍽 licensed 🎋 (outdoor) ♿ toilets for disabled shop 🚫

WAKEFIELD

Wakefield Art Gallery

Wentworth Ter WF1 3QW
☎ 01924 305796 📠 01924 305770
e-mail: museumsandarts@wakefield.gov.uk
web: www.wakefield.gov.uk/cultureandleisure
dir: N of city centre by Wakefield College and Clayton Hospital

Wakefield was home to two of Britain's greatest modern sculptors - Barbara Hepworth and Henry Moore. The art gallery, which has an important collection of 20th-century paintings and sculptures, has a special room devoted to these two local artists. There are frequent temporary exhibitions of both modern and earlier works.

Times Open all year, Tue-Sat 10.30-4.30, Sun 2-4.30.* Facilities 🅿 🎋 (outdoor) ♿ (partly accessible) shop 🚫

VALE

Rousse Tower

Rousse Tower Headland
☎ 01489 726518 & 726965
📄 01481 715177
e-mail: admin@museums.gov.gg
web: www.museums.gov.gg
dir: on Island's W coast, signed

One of the original fifteen towers built in 1778-9
in prime defensive positions around the coast
of Guernsey. Recently re-furbished, they were
designed primarily to prevent the landing of
troops on nearby beaches. Musket fire could
be directed on invading forces through the
loopholes. An interpretation centre displays
replica guns.

Times Open Apr-Oct 9-dusk, Nov-Mar, Wed, Sat &
Sun 9-4. Facilities ℗ Ⓟ ♿ (partly accessible)
(tower can only be viewed from the outside) 🚫

LA GREVE DE LECQ

Greve de Lecq Barracks

☎ 01534 483193 & 482238
📄 01534 485434
e-mail: enquiries@nationaltrustjersey.org.je
web: www.nationaltrustjersey.org.je
dir: on side of valley, overlooking beach

Originally serving as an outpost of the British
Empire, these barracks, built in 1810, were used
for civilian housing from the end of WWI to 1972,
when they were bought by the National Trust
and made into a museum that depicts the life
of soldiers who were stationed here in the 19th
century. Also includes a collection of old horse-
drawn carriages.

Times Open May-Sep, Wed-Sat, 10-4, Sun 1-4.*
Facilities ℗ Ⓟ ♿ toilets for disabled shop
🚫 🚃

CASTLETOWN

Old Grammar School

IM9 1LE

☎ 01624 648000   📄 01624 648001
e-mail: enquiries@mnh.gov.im
web: www.storyofmann.com
dir: centre of Castletown, opposite the castle

Built around 1200AD, the former capital's first church, St Mary's, has had a significant role in Manx education. It was a school from 1570 to 1930 and evokes memories of Victorian school life.

Times Open daily, Etr-late Oct, 10-5.*
Facilities 🅿 Ⓟ 🍴 (outdoor) ♿ (partly accessible) (restricted access narrow door, 3 steps) shop ⊗

DOUGLAS

Manx Museum

IM1 3LY

☎ 01624 648000   📄 01624 648001
e-mail: enquiries@mnh.gov.im
web: www.storyofmann.com
dir: signed in Douglas

The Island's treasure house provides an exciting introduction to the "Story of Mann" where a specially produced film portrayal of Manx history complements the award-winning displays. Galleries depict natural history, archaeology and the social development of the Island. There are also examples of famous Manx artists in the National Art Gallery, together with the Island's National archive and reference library. Events and exhibitions throughout the year, please visit website for details.

Times Open all year, Mon-Sat, 10-5. Closed 25-26 Dec & 1 Jan.* Facilities 🅿 Ⓟ 🖥🍴 licensed 🍴 (outdoor) ♿ toilets for disabled shop ⊗

PORT ST MARY

Sound Visitor Centre

The Sound IM1 3LY

☎ 01624 648000 & 838123

📠 01624 648001

e-mail: enquiries@mnh.gov.im

web: www.storyofmann.com

dir: follow coastal road towards Port Erin/Port St Mary. Past Cregneash village towards most S point of Island

The Sound Visitor Centre is set in one of the Island's most scenic areas overlooking the natural wonders of the Sound and the Calf of Man. Along with information and audio presentations about the area, other facilities add to the enjoyment and convenience of visitors.

Times Open daily, Etr-Oct 10-5. For winter opening times telephone 01624 838123.*
Facilities ℗ 🍴 licensed 🎪 (outdoor) ♿ toilets for disabled ⊗

ABERDEEN

Aberdeen Art Gallery

Schoolhill AB10 1FQ

☎ 01224 523700 📠 01224 632133

e-mail: info@aagm.co.uk

web: www.aberdeencity.gov.uk

dir: located in city centre

Aberdeen's splendid art gallery houses an important fine art collection, a rich and diverse applied art collection and an exciting programme of special exhibitions.

Times Open all year Tue-Sat 10-5, Sun 2-5. Closed Xmas & New Year* Facilities ℗ toilets for disabled shop ⊗

ABERDEEN

Aberdeen Maritime Museum

Shiprow AB11 5BY

☎ 01224 337700   🖹 01224 213066
e-mail: info@aagm.co.uk
web: www.aberdeencity.gov.uk
dir: located in city centre

The award-winning Maritime Museum brings the history of the North Sea to life. Featuring displays and exhibitions on the offshore oil industry, shipbuilding, fishing and clipper ships.

Times Open all year, Tue-Sat, 10-5, Sun 2-5.* Facilities ℗ 🗗 🍽 licensed ♿ (partly accessible) (2 rooms in Provost Ross's house not accessible due to stairs) toilets for disabled shop ⊗

ABERDEEN

Cruickshank Botanic Garden

The Chanonry AB24 3UU

☎ 01224 272704   🖹 01224 272703
web: http://www.abdn.ac.uk/pss/cruickshank
dir: enter by gate in Chanonry, in Old Aberdeen

Developed at the end of the 19th century, the 11 acres include rock and water gardens, a rose garden, a fine herbaceous border, an arboretum and a patio garden. There are collections of spring bulbs, gentians and alpine plants, and a fine array of trees and shrubs.

Times Open all year, Mon-Fri 9-4.30; also Sat & Sun, May-Sep 2-5.* Facilities ℗ ♿ (partly accessible) (some steep, narrow paths) ⊗

ABERDEEN

Provost Skene's House

Guestrow, off Broad St AB10 1AS

☎ 01224 641086

e-mail: info@aagm.co.uk

web: www.aberdeencity.gov.uk

dir: located in town centre

16th century town house with a stunning series of period room settings. Painted Gallery and changing displays of local history.

Times Open all year Mon-Sat 10-5.* Facilities Ⓟ 🖵 ⊗

BANCHORY

Banchory Museum

Bridge St AB31 5SX

☎ 01771 622807   🖹 01771 623558

e-mail: heritage@aberdeenshire.gov.uk

web: www.aberdeenshire.gov.uk/museums

dir: in Bridge St beside tourist information centre

The museum has displays on Scott Skinner (The 'Strathspey King'), natural history, royal commemorative china, local silver artefacts and a variety of local history displays.

Times Open Jan-Jun & Sep-Dec, Mon, Fri-Sat 11-1 & 2-4; Jul-Aug, Mon-Wed & Fri-Sat, 11-1, 2-4.* Facilities Ⓟ ♿ toilets for disabled ⊗

BANFF

Banff Museum

High St AB45 1AE

☎ 01771 622807   📠 01771 623558

e-mail: museums@aberdeenshire.gov.uk

web: www.aberdeenshire.gov.uk/museums

Displays of geology, natural history, local history, Banff silver, arms and armour, and displays relating to James Ferguson (18th-century astronomer) and Thomas Edward (19th-century Banff naturalist).

Times Open Jun-Sep, Mon-Sat 2-4.30.*

Facilities ℗ ♿ (partly accessible) (ground floor only accessible) ⊗

HUNTLY

Brander Museum

The Square AB54 8AE

☎ 01771 622807   📠 01771 623558

e-mail: heritage@aberdeenshire.gov.uk

web: www.@aberdeenshire.gov.uk/museums

dir: in centre of Huntly, sharing building with library, museum on ground floor

The museum has displays of local and church history, plus the 19th-century Anderson Bey and the Sudanese campaigns. Exhibits connected with George MacDonald, author and playwright, can also be seen.

Times Open all year, Tue-Sat 2-4.30.*

Facilities ℗ ♿ ⊗

INVERURIE

Carnegie Museum

Town House, The Square AB51 3SN
☎ 01771 622807   🖹 01771 623558
e-mail: museums@aberdeenshire.gov.uk
web: www.aberdeenshire.gov.uk/museums
dir: in centre of Inverurie, on left side of
townhouse building, above library

This fine museum contains displays on local
history and archaeology, including Pictish stones,
Bronze Age material and the Great North of
Scotland Railway.

Times Open all year, Mon & Wed-Fri 2-4, Sat 10-1
& 2-4. Closed Tue & public hols.* Facilities ℗
🚹 ⊗

MINTLAW

Aberdeenshire Farming Museum

Aden Country Park AB42 5FQ
☎ 01771 624590   🖹 01771 623558
e-mail: museums@aberdeenshire.gov.uk
web: www.aberdeenshire.gov.uk/museums
dir: 1m W of Mintlaw on A950

Housed in 19th-century farm buildings, once
part of the estate which now makes up the Aden
Country Park. Two centuries of farming history
and innovation are illustrated, and the story of
the estate is also told. The reconstructed farm of
Hareshowe shows how a family in the north-east
farmed during the 1950s - access by guided
tour only.

Times Open May-Sep, daily 11-4.30; Apr & Oct,
wknds only noon-4.30. (Last admission 30 mins
before closing). Park open all year, Apr-Sep 7-10;
winter 7-7.* Facilities ❷ ℗ ⊡ ㅠ (outdoor)
🚹 (partly accessible) (1st floor not accessible)
toilets for disabled shop ⊗

OLD DEER

Deer Abbey

☎ 01667 460232
web: www.historic-scotland.gov.uk
dir: 2m W of Mintlaw on A950

The remains of the Cistercian Abbey, founded in 1218, include the infirmary, Abbot's House and the southern claustral range. The University Library at Cambridge now houses the famous Book of Deer.

Times Open Apr-Sep, daily, 9.30-5 and during daylight hrs in winter.* Facilities ℗ ⊗ ▮

PETERHEAD

Arbuthnot Museum

St Peter St AB42 1QD
☎ 01771 622807   📄 01771 623558
e-mail: museums@aberdeenshire.gov.uk
web: www.aberdeenshire.gov.uk/museums
dir: at St.Peter St & Queen St x-roads, above library

Specialising in local exhibits, particularly those relating to the fishing industry, this museum also displays Arctic and whaling specimens and a British coin collection. The regular programme of exhibitions changes approximately every six weeks.

Times Open all year, Mon-Tue & Thu-Sat 11-1 & 2-4.30, Wed 11-1. Closed Sun and BHs.* Facilities ℗ ⊗

Tolbooth Museum

Old Pier AB39 2JU
☎ 01771 622807   📄 01771 623558
e-mail: museums@aberdeenshire.gov.uk
web: www.aberdeenshire.gov.uk/museums
dir: on harbour front

Built in the late 16th century as a storehouse
for the Earls Marischal at Dunnottar Castle,
the building was the Kincardineshire County
Tollbooth from 1600-1767. Displays feature local
history and fishing.

Times Open 3 Apr-28 Sep, Wed-Mon, 1.30-4.30.*
Facilities ℗ ⊗

Arbroath Signal Tower Museum

Signal Tower, Ladyloan DD11 1PU
☎ 01241 875598   📄 01241 439263
e-mail: signal.tower@angus.gov.uk
web: www.angus.gov.uk/history/museums
dir: on A92 adjacent to harbour. 16m NE of
Dundee

Arbroath Smokies, textiles and engineering
feature at this local history museum housed in
the 1813 shore station of Stevenson's Bell Rock
lighthouse.

Times Open all year, Mon-Sat 10-5; Jul-Aug, Sun
2-5. Closed 25-26 Dec & 1-2 Jan. Facilities ℗
℗ 🍴 (outdoor) ♿ (partly accessible) (access
restricted to ground floor, no lift) shop ⊗

BRECHIN

Brechin Town House Museum

28 High St DD9 7AA

☎ 01356 625536

e-mail: brechin.museum@angus.gov.uk

web: www.angus.gov.uk/history/museum

dir: off A90 at sign for Brechin, 2m into town centre

Within a former courtroom, debtor's prison and seat of local government, this museum covers the history of the little City of Brechin from the earliest settlement, through the market town to industrialisation in the form of flax, jute mills, distilling, weaving and engineering. Brechin's fascinating history of development is portrayed in vivid displays. The Museum will be closed for refurbishment until April 2010.

Times Closed for refurbishment until Apr 2010 then open Mon-Tue & Thu-Sat 10-5, Wed 10-1. Closed 25-26 Dec, 1-2 Jan. Facilities Ⓟ ⅍ toilets for disabled shop ⊗

FORFAR

The Meffan Museum & Art Gallery

20 West High St DD8 1BB

☎ 01307 464123 & 467017

🖹 01307 468451

e-mail: the.meffan@angus.gov.uk

web: www.angus.gov/history/museum

dir: off A90. Attraction in town centre

This lively, ever-changing contemporary art gallery and museum is full of surprises. Walk down a cobbled street full of shops, ending up at a witch-burning scene. Carved Pictish stones and a diorama of an archaeological dig complete the vibrant displays.

Times Open all year Mon-Sat. Closed 25-26 Dec & 1-2 Jan. Facilities Ⓟ toilets for disabled shop ⊗

KIRRIEMUIR

Kirriemuir Gateway to the Glens Museum

The Town House, 32 High St DD8 4BB

☎ 01575 575479

e-mail: kirrie.gateway@angus.gov.uk
web: www.angus.gov.uk/history/museum
dir: in town centre square, 30mins from Dundee, N on A90

Housed in the town house dating from 1604, this museum covers the history of Kirriemuir and the Angus Glens from prehistoric times. A realistic model of Kirriemuir on market day in 1604 can be seen and local voices can be heard telling their part in the area's history from sweet making to linen weaving. Animals and birds can be seen at close range in the Wildlife diorama. The museum also houses Kirriemuir tourist information centre.

Times Open all year, Jan-Mar & Oct-Dec, Mon-Wed, Fri-Sat 10-5, Thu 2-5; Apr-Sep, Mon-Sat 10-5 Facilities ℗ ⚹ (partly accessible) (ground floor accessible, steps to first floor) toilets for disabled shop ⊗

MONTROSE

Montrose Museum & Art Gallery

Panmure Place DD10 8HE

☎ 01674 673232

e-mail: montrose.museum@angus.gov.uk
web: www.angus.gov.uk/history/museum
dir: opposite Montrose Academy in town centre, approach via A92 from Aberdeen or Dundee

Extensive local collections cover the history of Montrose from prehistoric times, the maritime history of the port, the natural history of Angus, and local art. The museum also houses Montrose tourist information centre. The museum will be closed for refurbishment until April 2010.

Times Closed for refurbishment until Apr 2010 then open all year, Mon-Sat 10-5. Closed 25-26 Dec & 1-2 Jan. Facilities ℗ ⚹ toilets for disabled shop ⊗

155

ARROCHAR

Argyll Forest Park

Forestry Commission, Ardgartan Visitor Centre
G83 7AR

☎ 01301 702597   📠 01301 702597
e-mail: katy.freeman@forestry.gsl.gov.uk
dir: on A83 at foot of "The Rest and Be Thankful"

This park extends over a large area of hill ground and forest, noted for its rugged beauty. Numerous forest walks and picnic sites allow exploration; the Arboretum walks and the route between Younger Botanic Gardens and Puck's Glen are particularly lovely. Wildlife viewing facilities include live footage of nesting birds in season.

Times Open Etr-Oct, daily.* Facilities ❷ 🎋 (outdoor) shop

CARNASSARIE CASTLE

Carnassarie Castle

PA31 8RQ
web: www.historic-scotland.gov.uk
dir: 2m N of Kilmartin off A816

A handsome combined tower house and hall, home of John Carswell, first Protestant Bishop of the Isles and translator of the first book printed in Gaelic. Very fine architectural details of the late 16th century.

Times Open at all reasonable times.*
Facilities ⊗ 🎋

KILMARTIN

Dunadd Fort

web: www.historic-scotland.gov.uk
dir: 2m S of Kilmartin on A816

Dunadd was one of the ancient capitals of Dalriada from which the Celtic kingdom of Scotland was formed. Near to this prehistoric hill fort (now little more than an isolated hillock) are carvings of a boar and a footprint; these probably marked the spot where early kings were invested with their royal power.

Times Open at all reasonable times.*
Facilities ⊗ 🎒

DRUMCOLTRAN TOWER

Drumcoltran Tower

web: www.historic-scotland.gov.uk
dir: 7m NE of Dalbeattie, in farm buildings off A711

A well-preserved tower from the mid-16th century, simply planned and built, set in a busy modern farmyard.

Times Open at any reasonable time.*
Facilities 🅿 ⊗ 🎒

DUMFRIES

Burns Mausoleum

St Michael's Churchyard
☎ 01387 255297   📄 01387 265081
e-mail: dumfriesmuseum@dumgal.gov.uk
web: www.dumgal.gov.uk/museums
dir: at junct of Brooms Rd (ATS) and St Michael's St (B725)

The mausoleum is in the form of a Greek temple, and contains the tombs of Robert Burns, his wife Jean Armour, and their five sons. A sculptured group shows the Muse of Poetry flinging her cloak over Burns at the plough.

Times House: Phone for details. Grounds: Unrestricted access.

DUMFRIES

Robert Burns House

Burns St DG1 2PS
☎ 01387 255297   📄 01387 265081
e-mail: dumfriesmuseum@dumgal.gov.uk
web: www.dumgal.gov.uk/museums
dir: signed from Brooms Rd [ATS] car park

It was in this house that Robert Burns spent the last three years of his short life; he died here in 1796. It retains much of its 18th-century character and contains many fascinating items connected with the poet. There is the chair in which he wrote his last poems, many original letters and manuscripts, and the famous Kilmarnock and Edinburgh editions of his work.

Times Open all year, Apr-Sep, Mon-Sat 10-5, Sun 2-5; Oct-Mar, Tue-Sat 10-1 & 2-5.* Fees Free admission but donations welcome Facilities ℗ shop

KIRKCUDBRIGHT

Stewartry Museum

St Mary St DG6 4AQ

☎ 01557 331643   ▤ 01557 331643

e-mail: david.devereux@dumgal.gov.uk

web: www.dumgal.gov.uk/museums

dir: from A711 through town, pass parish church, museum approx 200mtrs on right

A large and varied collection of archaeological, social history and natural history exhibits relating to the Stewartry district.

Times Open all year, May, Jun & Sep, Mon-Sat 11-5, Sun 2-5; Jul-Aug, Mon-Sat 10-5, Sun 2-5; Oct, Mon-Sat 11-4, Sun 2-5; Nov-Apr, Mon-Sat 11-4. Facilities ℗ ⊼ (outdoor) ♿ (partly accessible) (access to ground floor only) shop ⊗

KIRKCUDBRIGHT

Tolbooth Art Centre

High St DG6 4JL

☎ 01557 331556   ▤ 01557 331643

e-mail: david.devereux@dumgal.gov.uk

web: www.dumgal.gov.uk/museums

dir: from A711, through town pass parish church & Stewartry Museum, 1st right into High St

Dating from 1629, the Tolbooth was converted into an art centre and provides an interpretive introduction to the Kirkcudbright artists's colony, which flourished in the town from the 1880s. It also provides studio and exhibition space for contemporary local and visiting artists. There is a programme of exhibitions from March to October.

Times Open all year, May, Jun & Sep, Mon-Sat 11-5, Sun 2-5; Jul & Aug, Mon-Sat 10-5, Sun 2-5; Oct, Mon-Sat 11-4, Sun 2-5; Nov-Apr, Mon-Sat 11-4. Facilities ℗ ⊡ ♿ (partly accessible) (step to small studio) toilets for disabled shop ⊗

PALNACKIE

Orchardton Tower

web: www.historic-scotland.gov.uk
dir: 6m SE of Castle Douglas on A711

A charming little tower house from the mid-15th-century. It is, uniquely, circular in plan.

Times Open all reasonable times. Closed 25-26 Dec.* Facilities ❷ ⊗ ▮

RUTHWELL

Ruthwell Cross

☎ 131 550 7612
web: www.historic-scotland.gov.uk
dir: sited within the parish church on B724

Now in a specially built apse in the parish church, the carved cross dates from the 7th or 8th centuries. Two faces show scenes from the Life of Christ; the others show scroll work, and parts of an ancient poem in Runic characters. It was broken up in the 18th century, but pieced together by a 19th-century minister.

Times Open all reasonable times. Contact Key Keeper for access on 01387 870249.* Facilities ❷ ⊗ ▮

RUTHWELL

Savings Banks Museum

DG1 4NN

☎ 01387 870640

e-mail: savingsbanksmuseum@tiscali.co.uk
web: www.lloydstsb.com/savingsbankmuseum
dir: off B724, 10m E of Dumfries & 7m W of
Annan

Housed in the building where Savings Banks
first began, the museum traces their growth
and development from 1810 up to the present
day. The museum also traces the life of Dr Henry
Duncan, father of savings banks, and restorer
of the Ruthwell Cross. Multi-lingual leaflets
available.

Times Open all year, Apr-Sep, Tue-Sat; Oct-Mar,
Thu-Sat 10-4. Open on BHs except Xmas Day &
New Year.* Facilities 🅿 Ⓟ ♿ ⊗

SANQUHAR

Sanquhar Tolbooth Museum

High St DG4 6BN

☎ 01659 250186   📠 01387 265081

e-mail: dumfriesmuseum@dumgal.gov.uk
web: www.dumgal.gov.uk/museums
dir: on A76 Dumfries-Kilmarnock road

Housed in the town's fine 18th-century tolbooth,
the museum tells the story of the mines and
miners of the area, its earliest inhabitants,
native and Roman, the history and customs of
the Royal Burgh of Sanquhar and local traditions.

Times Open Apr-Sep, Tue-Sat 10-1 & 2-5 & Sun
2-5 . Facilities 🅿 Ⓟ shop

DUNDEE

Broughty Castle Museum

Castle Approach, Broughty Ferry DD5 2TF
☎ 01382 436916   📄 01382 436951
e-mail: broughty@dundeecity.gov.uk
web: www.dundeecity.gov.uk/broughtycastle
dir: turn S off A930 at traffic lights by Eastern
Primary School in Broughty Ferry

This 15th-century coastal fort has faced many
battles and sieges, and was rebuilt in the
19th century as part of the River Tay's coastal
defence system. It now houses a fascinating
museum featuring displays on the life and times
of Broughty Ferry, its people, the environment
and the wildlife that lives close by. Don't miss
the new gallery which features a selection of
paintings from the Orchar Collection - one of the
most important collections of Scottish Victorian
art in the country. Enjoy the spectacular views
over the River Tay.

Times Open all year Apr-Sep, Mon-Sat 10-4, Sun
12.30-4; Oct-Mar, Tue-Sat 10-4, Sun 12.30-4.
Closed Mons, 25-26 Dec & 1-3 Jan.* Facilities ℗
🖵 shop ⊗

KILMARNOCK

Dick Institute Museum & Art Galleries

Elmbank Ave KA1 3BU
☎ 01563 554343   📄 01563 554344
web: www.east-ayrshire.gov.uk
dir: follow brown tourist signs from A77 S of
Glasgow, into town centre

Temporary and permanent exhibitions spread
over two floors of this grand Victorian building.
Fine art, social and natural history feature
upstairs, whilst the downstairs galleries house
temporary exhibitions of art and craft.

Times Open all year, Tue-Sat 11-5. Closed Sun,
Mon and Public Hols.* Facilities ℗ ℗ 🚻 toilets
for disabled shop ⊗

BEARSDEN

Antonine Wall: Bearsden Bath-house

Roman Rd G61 2SG
web: www.historic-scotland.gov.uk
dir: signed from Bearsden Cross on A810

Considered to be the best surviving visible Roman building in Scotland, the bath-house was discovered in 1973 during excavations for a construction site. It was originally built for use by the Roman garrison at Bearsden Fort, which is part of the Antonine Wall defences. This building dates from the 2nd century AD. Visitors should wear sensible footwear.

Times Open all reasonable times.* Facilities ⊗ 🔖

MILNGAVIE

Mugdock Country Park

Craigallian Rd G62 8EL
☎ 0141 956 6100 & 6586
e-mail: rangers@mcp.ndo.co.uk
web: www.mugdock-country-park.org.uk
dir: N of Glasgow on A81, signed

This country park incorporates the remains of Mugdock and Craigend castles, set in beautiful landscapes as well as an exhibition centre, craft shops, orienteering course and many walks.

Times Open all year, daily.* Facilities 🅿 ⓟ 🍵 ⦿ licensed ⊓ (outdoor) toilets for disabled shop

EAST LINTON

Hailes Castle

web: www.historic-scotland.gov.uk
dir: 1.5m SW of East Linton on A1

A beautiful sited ruin incorporating a fortified
manor of 13th-century date, extended in the
14th and 15th centuries. There are two vaulted
pit-prisons.

Times Open at all reasonable times.*
Facilities ❷ ⊼ ⊗ ▤

PRESTONPANS

Prestongrange Museum

Prestongrange
☎ 0131 653 2904   📄 01620 828201
e-mail: elms@eastlothian.gov.uk
web: www.prestongrange.org
dir: on B1348 coast road between Prestonpans &
Musselburgh

The oldest documented coal mining site in
Scotland, with 800 years of history, this museum
shows a Cornish Beam Engine and on-site
evidence of associated industries such as
brickmaking and pottery. It is located next to a
16th-century customs port. Contact for details of
special events or see website.

Times Open Apr-Oct, daily, 11-4.30. Facilities ❷
⊡ ⊼ (outdoor) ♿ (partly accessible) (grounds
partly accessible) toilets for disabled shop ⊗

EDINBURGH

City Art Centre

2 Market St EH1 1DE
☎ 0131 529 3993 📄 0131 529 3977
e-mail: cityartcentre@edinburgh.gov.uk
web: www.cac.org.uk
dir: opposite rear of Waverley Stn

The City Art Centre houses the city's permanent fine art collection and stages a constantly changing programme of temporary exhibitions from all parts of the world. It has six floors of display galleries (linked by an escalator).

Times Open all year, Mon-Sat 10-5 & Sun 12-5*
Facilities ℗ 🚻 🍴 licensed ♿ toilets for disabled shop ⊗

EDINBURGH

Museum of Childhood

42 High St, Royal Mile EH1 1TG
☎ 0131 529 4142 📄 0131 558 3103
e-mail: moc@edinburgh.gov.uk
web: www.cac.org.uk
dir: On the Royal Mile

One of the first museums of its kind, this was the brainchild of a local councillor, and first opened in 1955. It has a wonderful collection of toys, games and other belongings of children through the ages, to delight visitors both old and young. Ring for details of special events.

Times Open all year, Mon-Sat 10-5, Sun 12-5.*
Facilities ℗ ♿ (partly accessible) toilets for disabled shop ⊗

EDINBURGH

Museum of Edinburgh

142 Canongate, Royal Mile EH8 8DD
☎ 0131 529 4143 📄 0131 557 3346
e-mail: moe@edinburgh.gov.uk
web: www.cac.org.uk
dir: on the Royal Mile

Housed in one of the best-preserved 16th-century buildings in the Old Town. It was built in 1570 and later became the headquarters of the Incorporation of Hammermen. Now a museum of local history, it has collections of silver, glassware, pottery, and other items such as street signs.

Times Open all year, Mon-Sat 10-5. Sun in Aug noon-5.* Facilities ⓟ toilets for disabled shop ⊗

EDINBURGH

National Museum of Scotland

Chambers St EH1 1JF
☎ 0131 225 7534
e-mail: info@nms.ac.uk
web: www.nms.ac.uk
dir: situated in Chambers St in Old Town. A few mins walk from Princes St and The Royal Mile

Scotland - past, present and future. The Museum's collections tell you the story of Scotland - land, people and culture. What influence has the world had on Scotland, and Scotland on the world? Your journey of discovery starts here. For generations the museum has collected key exhibits from all over Scotland and beyond. Viking brooches, Pictish stones, ancient chessmen and Queen Mary's clarsach. There's more! Connect with Dolly the sheep, design a robot, test drive a Formula One car or blast off into outer space. See website for special exhibitions and events. Part of the Victorian Royal museum building is closed for refurbishment and will re-open in 2011.

Times Open all year, daily 10-5. Facilities ⓟ ☕ 🍽 licensed ♿ toilets for disabled shop ⊗

EDINBURGH

Parliament House

Supreme Courts, 2-11 Parliament Square
EH1 1RQ

☎ 0131 225 2595   🖹 0131 240 6755
e-mail: emackenzie@scotcourts.gov.uk
web: www.scotcourts.gov.uk
dir: behind St Giles Cathedral on the high street

Scotland's independent parliament last sat
in 1707, in this 17th-century building hidden
behind an 1829 façade, now the seat of the
Supreme Law Courts of Scotland. A large stained
glass window depicts the inauguration of the
Court of Session in 1540.

Times Open all year, Mon-Fri 10-4.* Facilities ℗
🖵 🍽 licensed toilets for disabled ⊗

EDINBURGH

The People's Story Museum

Canongate Tolbooth, 163 Canongate, Royal
Mile EH8 8BN

☎ 0131 529 4057   🖹 0131 556 3439
e-mail: socialhistory@edinburgh.gov.uk
web: www.cac.org.uk
dir: on the Royal Mile

The museum, housed in the 16th-century
tolbooth, tells the story of the ordinary people
of Edinburgh from the late 18th century to the
present day. Reconstructions include a prison
cell, 1930s pub and 1940s kitchen supported by
photographs, displays, sounds and smells.

Times Open all year, Mon-Sat 10-5. Also open
Sun in Aug 12-5. Facilities ℗ ♿ (partly
accessible) (wheelchair accessible) toilets for
disabled ⊗

EDINBURGH

Royal Botanic Garden Edinburgh

Inverleith Row EH3 5LR

☎ 0131 552 7171   📄 0131 248 2901

e-mail: info@rbge.org.uk

web: www.rbge.org.uk

dir: 1m N of city centre, off A902

Established in 1670, on an area the size of a tennis court, the Garden is now over 70 acres of beautifully landscaped grounds. Spectacular features include the Rock Garden and the Chinese Hillside. The amazing glasshouses feature Britain's tallest palm house and the magnificent woodland gardens and arboretum.

Times Open all year, daily; Apr-Sep, 10-7; Mar & Oct, 10-6; Nov-Feb, 10-4. Closed 25 Dec & 1 Jan. (Facilities close 30 mins before Garden)* Facilities ℗ ☕ 🍽 licensed toilets for disabled shop ⊗

EDINBURGH

Scottish National Gallery of Modern Art

75 Belford Rd EH4 3DR

☎ 0131 624 6200   📄 0131 343 3250

e-mail: enquiries@nationalgalleries.org

web: www.nationalgalleries.org

dir: in West End, 20min walk from Haymarket station

An outstanding collection of 20th-century painting, sculpture and graphic art. Includes major works by Matisse, Picasso, Bacon, Moore and Lichtenstein and an exceptional group of Scottish paintings. Set in leafy grounds with a sculpture garden.

Times Open all year, daily 10-5. New Year's Day noon-5. Closed 25-26 Dec. Fees Free. Admission charged to some major exhibitions. Facilities ℗ ☕ ♿ toilets for disabled shop ⊗

EDINBURGH

The Writers' Museum

Lady Stair's House, Lady Stair's Close,
Lawnmarket EH1 2PA
☎ 0131 529 4901   ▤ 0131 220 5057
e-mail: writersmuseum@edinburgh.gov.uk
web: www.cac.org.uk
dir: off the Royal Mile

Situated in the historic Lady Stair's House which
dates from 1622, the museum houses various
objects associated with Robert Burns, Sir Walter
Scott and Robert Louis Stevenson. Temporary
exhibitions are planned throughout the year.

Times Open all year, Mon-Sat 10-5. (Aug only,
Sun 12-5). Facilities ℗ shop ⊗

SOUTH QUEENSFERRY

Queensferry Museum

53 High St EH30 9HP
☎ 0131 331 5545   ▤ 0131 557 3346
web: www.cac.org.uk
dir: A90 from Edinburgh

The museum commands magnificent views of the
two great bridges spanning the Forth and traces
the history of the people of Queensferry and
Dalmeny, the historic ferry passage to Fife, the
construction of the rail and road bridges and the
wildlife of the Forth estuary. An ancient annual
custom, in August, is Burry Man, who is clad from
head to toe in burrs, and parades through the
town. See the full size model of the Burry Man in
the museum.

Times Open all year, Mon & Thu-Sat 10-1,
2.15-5, Sun noon-5. (Last admission 1/2 hour
before closing). Closed 25-26 Dec & 1-2 Jan
Facilities ℗ shop ⊗

BO'NESS

Kinneil Museum & Roman Fortlet

Duchess Anne Cottages, Kinneil Estate
EH51 0PR

☎ 01506 778530

web: www.falkirk.gov.uk/cultural

dir: follow tourist signs from Heritage Railway, off M9. Establishment at E end of town accessed via Dean Rd

The museum is in a converted stable block of Kinneil House. The ground floor has displays on the industrial history of Bo'ness, while the upper floor looks at the history and environment of the Kinneil Estate. The remains of the Roman fortlet can be seen nearby. An audio-visual presentation shows 2000 years of history.

Times Open all year, Mon-Sat 12.30-4.*
Facilities ❷ shop ⊗

FALKIRK

Callendar House

Callendar Park FK1 1YR

☎ 01324 503770   📄 01324 503771

e-mail: callendar.house@falkirk.gov.uk

web: www.falkirk.gov.uk/cultural

dir: On southside of town centre, Callendar House is signposted. Easily accessible from M9

Mary, Queen of Scots, Oliver Cromwell, Bonnie Prince Charlie, noble earls and wealthy merchants all feature in the history of Callendar House. Costumed interpreters describe early 19th-century life in the kitchens and the 900-year history of the house is illustrated in the 'Story of Callendar House' exhibition. The house is set in parkland, offering boating and woodland walks. Regular temporary heritage, natural history and visual arts exhibitions in Callendar House's Large Gallery.

Times Open all year, Mon-Sat, 10-5 (Sun Apr-Sep only 2-5).* Facilities ❷ Ⓟ ⊒ㅈ (outdoor) ♿ (partly accessible) (ramped access, lift to all floors, no wheelchair access to shop/reception) toilets for disabled shop ⊗

FALKIRK

Rough Castle

web: www.historic-scotland.gov.uk
dir: 1m E of Bonnybridge, signed from B816

The impressive earthworks of a large Roman fort on the Antonine Wall can be seen here. The buildings have disappeared, but the mounds and terraces are the sites of barracks, and granary and bath buildings. Running between them is the military road, which once linked all the forts on the wall and is still well defined.

Times Open any reasonable time.* Facilities **P**
⊗ 🗮

BURNTISLAND

Burntisland Edwardian Fair Museum

102 High St KY3 9AS
☎ 01592 583213
e-mail: kirkcaldy.museum@fife.gov.uk
dir: in the centre of Burntisland

Burntisland Museum has recreated a walk through the sights and sounds of the town's fair in 1910, based on a painting of the scene by local artist Andrew Young. See reconstructed rides, stalls and side shows of the time.

Times Open all year, Mon, Wed, Fri & Sat 10-1 & 2-5; Tue & Thu 10-1 & 2-7. Closed public hols* Facilities **P** ⊗

DUNFERMLINE

Andrew Carnegie Birthplace Museum

Moodie St KY12 7PL

☎ 01383 724302   📄 01383 749799

e-mail: info@carnegiebirthplace.com

web: www.carnegiebirthplace.com

dir: 400yds S from Abbey

The museum tells the story of the handloom weaver's son, born here in 1835, who created the biggest steel works in the USA and then became a philanthropist on a huge scale. The present-day work of the philanthropic Carnegie Trust is also explained. 175th anniversary of the birth of Andrew Carnegie on 25th November 2010.

Times Open Apr-Oct, Mon-Sat 11-5, Sun 2-5. Facilities ❷ ℗ ⬚& (partly accessible) (cottage inaccessible, main hall and shop accessible) toilets for disabled shop ⊗

DUNFERMLINE

Pittencrieff House Museum

Pittencrieff Park KY12 8QH

☎ 01383 722935   & 313838

📄 01383 313837

e-mail: dunfermline.museum@fife.gov.uk

dir: off A994 into Pittencriefff Park Car Park. Attraction on W edge of town

A fine 17th-century house standing in the beautiful park gifted to the town by Andrew Carnegie. Accessible displays tell the story of the park's animals and plants, with plenty of photographs of people enjoying the park over the last 100 years.

Times Open all year, daily Jan-Mar 11-4; Apr-Sep 11-5; Oct-Dec 11-4* Facilities ℗ & toilets for disabled shop ⊗

KIRKCALDY

Kirkcaldy Museum & Art Gallery

War Memorial Gardens KY1 1YG
☎ 01592 583213
e-mail: kirkcaldy.museum@fife.gov.uk
web: www.fifedirect.org.uk/museums
dir: next to train station

Set in the town's lovely memorial gardens, the museum houses a collection of fine and decorative art, including 18th to 21st-century Scottish paintings, among them the works of William McTaggart and S J Peploe. An award-winning display 'Changing Places' tells the story of the social, industrial and natural heritage of the area.

Times Open all year, Mon-Sat 10.30-5, Sun 2-5. Closed local hols* Facilities ❷ ℗ ⏁ & toilets for disabled shop ⊗

GLASGOW

Burrell Collection

Pollok Country Park, 2060 Pollokshaws Rd
G43 1AT
☎ 0141 287 2550 🖹 0141 287 2597
e-mail: museums@csglasgow.org
web: www.glasgowmuseums.com
dir: 3.5m S of city centre, signposted from M77 junct 2

Set in Pollok Country Park, this award-winning building makes the priceless works of art on display seem almost part of the woodland setting. Shipping magnate Sir William Burrell's main interests were medieval Europe, Oriental art and European paintings. Colourful paintings and stained glass show the details of medieval life. Furniture, paintings, sculpture, armour and weapons help to complete the picture. Rugs, ceramics and metalwork represent the art of Islam. There is also a strong collection of Chinese and other Oriental ceramics. Paintings on display include works by Bellini, Rembrandt and the French Impressionists.

Times Open all year, Mon-Thu & Sat 10-5, Fri & Sun 11-5. Closed 25-26 & 31 (pm) Dec & 1-2 Jan Facilities ❷ ⏁ ⏨ licensed & toilets for disabled shop ⊗

GLASGOW

Gallery of Modern Art

Royal Exchange Square G1 3AH
☎ 0141 287 3050   🖷 0141 287 3062
e-mail: museums@csglasgow.org
web: www.glasgowmuseums.com
dir: just off Buchanan St & close to Central
Station & Queen St Stn

GoMA offers a thought-provoking programme of
temporary exhibitions and workshops. It displays
work by local and international artists, as well as
addressing contemporary social issues through
its major biennial projects.

Times Open all year, Mon-Tue & Sat 10-5, Thu
10-8, Fri & Sun 11-5. Closed 25-26 Dec, 31 Dec
pm, 1-2 Jan. Fees Free entry donations welcome
Facilities ℗ ⊑ & toilets for disabled shop ⊗

GLASGOW

Glasgow Botanic Gardens

730 Great Western Rd G12 0UE
☎ 0141 276 1614   🖷 0141 276 1615
e-mail: gbg@land.glasgow.gov.uk
dir: From M8 junct 17 onto A82 Dumbarton.
Approx 2-3m the Botanic Gardens are on the right

Home of the national collections of Dendrobium
Orchids, Begonias and tree ferns, the Gardens
consist of an arboretum, herbaceous borders,
a herb garden, rose garden, and unusual
vegetables. The Kibble Palace contains
carnivorous plants, island flora and temperate
plant collections.

Times Open all year. Gardens open daily 7-dusk.
Glasshouses 10-6 (4.15 in winter).* Facilities ℗
toilets for disabled ⊗

GLASGOW

Glasgow Cathedral

Castle St G4 0QZ
☎ 0141 552 6891
web: www.historic-scotland.gov.uk
dir: M8 junct 15, in centre of Glasgow

The only Scottish mainland medieval cathedral to
have survived the Reformation complete (apart
from its western towers). Built during the 13th to
15th centuries over the supposed site of the tomb
of St Kentigern. Notable features in this splendid
building are the elaborately vaulted crypt, which
includes an introductory display and collection of
carved stones, the stone screen of the early 15th
century and the unfinished Blackadder Aisle.

Times Open all year, Apr-Sep, daily, 9.30-5.30,
Sun, 1-5; Oct-Mar, daily, 9.30-4.30, Sun 1-4.30.
Closed 25-26 Dec & 1-2 Jan.* Facilities shop
⊗ 🔖

GLASGOW

Glasgow Museums Resource Centre

200 Woodhead Rd, South Nitshill Ind Estate
G53 7NN
☎ 0141 276 9300   ▤ 0141 276 9305
web: www.glasgowmuseums.com
dir: on S side, close to Rail Stn

GMRC is the first publicly-accessible store for
the city's museum service, offering a behind-the-
scenes look at 200,000 treasures held in storage.
Please note that access to the stores is by guided
tour only. Viewings of a specific object can be
arranged, with two weeks prior notice. Activities,
tours and talks are held throughout the year - see
website or phone for details.

Times Open all year Mon-Thu & Sat 10-5, Fri-Sun
11-5. Guided tours for public at 2.30 Access is
only by guided tours.* Facilities ❷ toilets for
disabled ⊗

GLASGOW

Hunterian Art Gallery

82 Hillhead St, The University of Glasgow
G12 8QQ

☎ 0141 330 5431   🖹 0141 330 3618
e-mail: hunter@museum.gla.ac.uk
web: www.hunterian.gla.ac.uk
dir: on University of Glasgow Campus in Hillhead
District, 2m W of city centre

The founding collection is made up of paintings
bequeathed in the 18th century by Dr William
Hunter, including works by Rembrandt and
Stubbs. The Gallery now has works by James
McNeill Whistler, major displays of paintings by
the Scottish Colourists, and a graphics collection
holding some 300,000 prints. A popular feature
of the Charles Rennie Mackintosh collection
is the re-construction of the interiors of The
Mackintosh House.

Times Open all year, Mon-Sat 9.30-5. Telephone
for BH closures.* Facilities Ⓟ   ⌴ toilets for
disabled shop ⊗

GLASGOW

Hunterian Museum

Gilbert Scott Building, The University of
Glasgow G12 8QQ

☎ 0141 330 4221   🖹 0141 330 3617
e-mail: hunter@museum.gla.ac.uk
web: www.hunterian.gla.ac.uk
dir: on University of Glasgow campus in Hillhead
District, 2m W of city centre

Named after the 18th-century physician, Dr
William Hunter, who bequeathed his large and
important collections of coins, medals, fossils,
geological specimens and archaeological and
ethnographic items to the university. The exhibits
are shown in the main building of the university,
and temporary exhibitions are held.

Times Open all year, Mon-Sat 9.30-5. Closed
certain BHs phone for details.* Facilities Ⓟ
toilets for disabled shop ⊗

GLASGOW

Hutchesons' Hall

158 Ingram St G1 1EJ
☎ 0844 493 2199 📠 0844 493 2198
e-mail: information@nts.org.uk
web: www.nts.org.uk
dir: near SE corner of George Square

This handsome early 19th-century building
was designed by David Hamilton and houses a
visitor centre and shop. There is a video about
Glasgow's merchant city, and the Hall can be
booked for functions. Telephone for details of
concerts, recitals, etc. The Trust is considering
some new initiatives at Hutchesons' Hall and as
a result opening times may change. Please call in
advance before making a visit.

Times Please call in advance to check opening
times.* Facilities ℗ ♿ (partly accessible)
toilets for disabled shop ⊗ 🍽

GLASGOW

Kelvingrove Art Gallery & Museum

Argyle St G3 8AG
☎ 0141 276 9599 📠 0141 276 9540
e-mail: museums@csglasgow.org
web: www.glasgowmuseums.com
dir: 1m W of city centre

Glasgow's favourite building re-opened in July
2006 after a three-year, £35 million restoration
project. On display are 8000 objects, including a
Spitfire, a 4-metre ceratosaur and Salvador Dali's
Christ of St John of the Cross. A new 'Mackintosh
and the Glasgow Style Gallery' explores the
genius of Charles Rennie Mackintosh. Exciting
temporary exhibitions take place throughout the
year. Organ recitals take place each day and
there are a range of tours and activities available
for all ages.

Times Open all year, Mon-Thu & Sat 10-5; Fri &
Sun 11-5. Closed 25-26 Dec & 31 Dec (pm) & 1-2
Jan. Fees Free admission to venue & permanent
displays, some exhibitions have an entrance fee.
Please check website for details. Facilities ℗
℗ 🖵 🍽 licensed 🍴 (outdoor) ♿ toilets for
disabled shop ⊗

177

GLASGOW

Museum of Transport

1 Bunhouse Rd G3 8DP
☎ 0141 287 2720   📠 0141 287 2692
e-mail: museums@csglasgow.org
web: www.glasgowmuseums.com
dir: 1.5m W of city centre

Visit the Museum of Transport and the first impression is of gleaming metalwork and bright paint. All around you there are cars, caravans, carriages and carts, fire engines, buses, steam locomotives, prams and trams. The museum uses its collections of vehicles and models to tell the story of transport by land and sea, with a unique Glasgow flavour. Visitors can even go window shopping along the recreated Kelvin Street of 1938. Upstairs 250 ship models tell the story of the great days of Clyde shipbuilding. The Museum of Transport has something for everyone.

Times Open all year, Mon-Thu & Sat 10-5, Fri & Sun 11-5 until Apr 2010 when museum closes due to collections moving to a new museum.
Facilities 🅿 🅟 ⌨ ♿ toilets for disabled shop ⊗

GLASGOW

People's Palace

Glasgow Green G40 1AT
☎ 0141 276 0788   📠 0141 276 0787
e-mail: museums@csglasgow.org
web: www.glasgowmuseums.com
dir: 1m SE of city centre

Glasgow grew from a medieval town located by the Cathedral to the Second City of the British Empire. Trade with the Americas, and later industry, made the city rich. But not everyone shared in Glasgow's wealth. The People's Palace on historic Glasgow Green shows how ordinary Glaswegians worked, lived and played. Visitors can discover how a family lived in a typical one-room Glasgow 'single end' tenement flat, see Billy Connolly's amazing banana boots, learn to speak Glesga, take a trip 'doon the watter' and visit the Winter Gardens.

Times Open all year, Mon-Thu & Sat 10-5, Fri & Sun 11-5. Closed 25-26 & 31 Dec (pm) & 1-2 Jan
Facilities 🅟 ♿ toilets for disabled shop ⊗

GLASGOW

Provand's Lordship

3 Castle St G4 0RB

☎ 0141 552 8819   🖷 0141 552 4744

e-mail: museums@csglasgow.org

web: www.glasgowmuseums.com

dir: 1m E of city centre

Provand's Lordship is the only house to survive from Medieval Glasgow. For over 500 years it has watched the changing fortunes of the city and the nearby Cathedral. Bishop Andrew Muirhead built the house as part of St Nicholas' Hospital in 1571. The prebendary of Barlanark later bought it for use as a manse. Inside, the displays recreate home life in the middle ages. Behind the house is the St Nicholas Garden, built in 1997. It is a medical herb garden, in keeping with the original purpose of the house.

Times Open all year, Mon-Thu & Sat 10-5, Fri & Sun 11-5. Closed 25-26 Dec, 31 Dec pm, 1-2 Jan.* Facilities ℗ ♿ (partly accessible) (ground floor only) ⊗

GLASGOW

St Mungo Museum of Religious Life & Art

2 Castle St G4 0RH

☎ 0141 276 1625   🖷 0141 276 1626

e-mail: museums@csglasgow.org

web: www.glasgowmuseums.com

dir: 1m NE of city centre

The award-winning St Mungo Museum explores the importance of religion in peoples' everyday lives and art. It aims to promote understanding and respect between people of different faiths and of none. The museum features stained glass, objects, statues and video footage. In the grounds is Britain's first Japanese Zen garden.

Times Open all year, Mon-Thu & Sat 10-5, Fri & Sun 11-5. Closed 25-26 Dec, 31 Dec (pm) & 1-2 Jan. Facilities ℗ ☐ ♿ toilets for disabled shop ⊗

Scotland Street School Museum

225 Scotland St G5 8QB
☎ 0141 287 0500   📠 0141 287 0515
e-mail: museums@csglasgow.org
web: www.glasgowmuseums.com

Designed by Charles Rennie Mackintosh between 1903 and 1906 for the School Board of Glasgow, and now a museum telling the story of education in Scotland from 1872 to the late 20th century. Also hosts temporary exhibitions.

Times Open all year daily 10-5, Fri & Sun 11-5. (closed 25,26,31 Dec & pm 1 & 2 Jan)
Facilities ℗ ⬠♿ toilets for disabled shop ⊗

Clava Cairns

☎ 01667 460232
web: www.historic-scotland.gov.uk
dir: 6m E of Inverness, signed from B9091

A well-preserved Bronze Age cemetery complex of passage graves, ring cairns, kerb cairn and standing stones in a beautiful setting. In addition, the remains of a chapel of unknown date can be seen at this site.

Times Open at all reasonable times.*
Facilities ℗ ⊗▮

FORT WILLIAM

Inverlochy Castle

PH33 6SN
web: www.historic-scotland.gov.uk
dir: 2m NE of Fort William, off A82

A fine well-preserved 13th-century castle of the Comyn family; in the form of a square, with round towers at the corners. The largest tower was the donjon or keep. This is one of Scotland's earliest castles.

Times Open at all reasonable times.*
Facilities 🅿 ⊗ 🚩

KINGUSSIE

Ruthven Barracks

☎ 01667 460232
web: www.historic-scotland.gov.uk
dir: 1m SE from Kingussie, signed from A9 and A86

An infantry barracks erected in 1719 following the Jacobite rising of 1715, with two ranges of quarters and a stable block. Captured and burnt by Prince Charles Edward Stuart's army in 1746.

Times Open at any reasonable time.*
Facilities 🅿 ⊗ 🚩

NEWTONMORE

Highland Folk Museum

Aultlarie Croft PH20 1AY
☎ 01540 673551 📠 01540 673693
e-mail: highland.folk@highland.gov.uk
web: www.highlandfolk.com
dir: on A86, follow signs off A9

An early 18th-century farming township with turf houses has been reconstructed at this award-winning museum. A 1930s school houses old world maps, little wooden desks and a teacher rules! Other attractions include a working croft and tailor's workshop. Squirrels thrive in the pinewoods and there is an extensive play area at reception. A vintage bus runs throughout the site.

Times Open daily Etr-Aug, 10.30-5.30; Sep-Oct, 11-4.30. Facilities 🅿 ⬚ 🍴 (outdoor) toilets for disabled shop ⊗

ROSEMARKIE

Groam House Museum

High St IV10 8UF
☎ 01381 620961 & 01463 811883
📠 01463 811883
e-mail: curator@groamhouse.org.uk
web: www.groamhouse.org.uk
dir: off A9 at Tore onto A832

Opened in 1980, this community-based museum explores the history, culture and crafts of the mysterious Picts, who faded from history over a thousand years ago. Visitors can see the Rosemarkie symbol-bearing cross-slab and other Pictish sculptured stones; a replica Pictish harp, and a collection of photographs of Pictish stones all over the country. Thanks to a generous donation, the museum now holds the George Bain Collection of Celtic art for the Scottish Nation. Annual exhibitions take place, often with loans from other major museums.

Times Open Etr week, daily 2-4.30; closed Jan-Feb; May-Oct, Mon-Sat, 10-5, Sun 2-4.30; Apr, Sat-Sun 2-4.30. Nov-mid Dec, Sat-Sun 2-4 Facilities 🅿 Ⓟ ♿ (partly accessible) (wheelchair access to ground floor only) shop ⊗

WICK

Castle of Old Wick

☎ 01667 460232
web: www.historic-scotland.gov.uk
dir: 1m S on Shore Rd

The ruin of the best-preserved Norse castle in Scotland. Dating from the 12th-century this spectacular site is on a spine of rock projecting into the sea, between two deep, narrow gullies. Visitors must take great care and wear sensible shoes.

Times Open at all reasonable times.*
Facilities ⊗ 🚩

GREENOCK

McLean Museum & Art Gallery

15 Kelly St PA16 8JX
☎ 01475 715624
e-mail: museum@inverclyde.gov.uk
web: www.inverclyde.gov.uk/
dir: close to Greenock West Railway Station and Greenock Bus Station

James Watt was born in Greenock, and various exhibits connected with him are shown. The museum also has an art collection, and displays on shipping, local and natural history, Egyptology and ethnography.

Times Open all year, Mon-Sat 10-5. Closed some local & national PHs.* Facilities ℗ ㊐ (partly accessible) (only ground floor accessible, ramped entrance with automatic doors) toilets for disabled shop ⊗

DUFFUS

Duffus Castle

☎ 01667 460232
web: www.historic-scotland.gov.uk
dir: 5m NW of Elgin on B9012 to Burghead

One of the finest examples of a motte and bailey castle in Scotland with a later, very fine, stone hall house and curtain wall. The original seat of the Moray family.

Times Open at all reasonable times.*
Facilities ● ⊗ ▮

ELGIN

Pluscarden Abbey

IV30 8UA
☎ 01343 890257   📄 01343 890258
web: www.pluscardenabbey.org
dir: 6m SW of Elgin on unclass road

The original monastery was founded in 1230 by King Alexander II for monks of the Valliscaulian order from Burgundy, but it later became a Benedictine house. Monastic life was abandoned after the Reformation and the house passed through a succession of lay owners until it was bought by the third Marquess of Bute in 1898. His third son, Lord Colum Crichton Stuart gave the monastery to the Benedictines of Prinknash Abbey near Gloucester, and monastic life was recommenced in 1948. Today there are about twenty monks who lead a life of prayer, study and manual work. The services in the Abbey church are sung in Latin with Gregorian chant and are all open to the public.

Times Open all year, daily 4.45am-8.30pm.*
Facilities ● ℗ ♿ toilets for disabled shop ⊗

FORRES

Sueno's Stone

☎ 01667 460232
web: www.historic-scotland.gov.uk
dir: E end of Forres, off A96

The most remarkable sculptured monument in Britain, probably a cenotaph, standing over 20 feet high and dating back to the end of the first millennium AD. Covered by a protective glass enclosure.

Times Open at all reasonable times.*
Facilities ● ⊗ ▮

SPEY BAY

The WDCS Wildlife Centre

IV32 7PJ
☎ 01343 829109 🖹 01343 829065
e-mail: enquiries@mfwc.co.uk
web: www.mfwc.co.uk
dir: off A96 onto B9014 at Fochabers, follow road approx 5m to village of Spey Bay. Turn left at Spey Bay Hotel and follow road for 500mtrs

The centre, owned and operated by the Whale and Dolphin Conservation Society, lies at the mouth of the River Spey and is housed in a former salmon fishing station, built in 1768. There is a free exhibition about the Moray Firth dolphins and the wildlife of Spey Bay. Visitors can browse through a well-stocked gift shop and enjoy refreshments in the cosy tea room.

Times Open Apr-Oct 10.30-5. Check for winter opening times* Facilities ● Ⓟ ⊑ 丹 (outdoor) toilets for disabled shop ⊗

SALTCOATS

North Ayrshire Museum

Manse St, Kirkgate KA21 5AA
☎ 01294 464174 📄 01294 464174
e-mail: namuseum@north-ayrshire.gov.uk
web: www.north-ayrshire.gov.uk/museums

This museum is housed in an 18th-century church, and features a rich variety of artefacts from the North Ayrshire area, including archaeological and social history material. There is a continuing programme of temporary exhibitions.

Times Open all year Tue-Sat, 10-1 & 2-5.*
Facilities Ⓟ ♿ toilets for disabled shop ⊗

COATBRIDGE

Summerlee Industrial Museum

Heritage Way, West Canal St ML5 1QD
☎ 01236 638460 📄 01236 638454
e-mail: museums@northlan.gov.uk
web: www.visitlanarkshire.com/summerlee
dir: follow main routes towards town centre, adjacent to Coatbridge central station

A 20-acre museum of social and industrial history centering on the remains of the Summerlee Ironworks which were put into blast in the 1830s. The exhibition hall features displays of social and industrial history including working machinery, hands-on activities and recreated workshop interiors. Outside, Summerlee operates the only working tram in Scotland, a coal mine and reconstructed miners' rows with interiors dating from 1840.

Times Open summer 10-5, winter 10-4.
Facilities Ⓟ Ⓟ ⊑ ⊼ (outdoor) ♿ (partly accessible) (coal mine tour not accessible, miner's cottages narrow doors and single step) toilets for disabled shop ⊗

MOTHERWELL

Motherwell Heritage Centre

High Rd ML1 3HU
☎ 01698 251000 📠 01698 268867
e-mail: museums@northlan.gov.uk
web: www.nlcmuseums.bravehost.com
dir: A723 for town centre. Left at top of hill, after pedestrian crossing and just before railway bridge

This award-winning audio-visual experience, 'Technopolis', traces the history of the area from Roman times to the rise of 19th-century industry and the post-industrial era. There is also a fine viewing tower, an exhibition gallery and family history research facilities. A mixed programme of community events and touring exhibitions occur throughout the year.

Times Open all year Wed-Sat 10-5 (Thu 10-7), Sun 12-5. Also open BHs. Local studies library closed Sun* Facilities ❷ ⓟ ♿ toilets for disabled shop ⊗

DUNKELD

The Ell Shop & Little Houses

The Cross PH8 0AN
☎ 0844 4932192
e-mail: information@nts.org.uk
web: www.nts.org.uk
dir: off A9, 15m N of Perth

The National Trust owns two rows of 20 houses in Dunkeld, and has preserved their 17th/18th-century character. They are not open to the public, but there is a display and audio-visual show in the Information Centre.

Times Open all year: Ell Shop: Apr-Oct, Mon-Sat 10-5.30, Sun 12.30-5.30, Nov-23 Dec, Mon-Sat 10-4.30, Sun 12.30-4.30. Closed for 30mins lunch. Riverbanks & Stanley Hill: all year, daily.* Facilities ⓟ ♿ (partly accessible) (small step into shop) toilets for disabled shop ⊗ ☒

KILLIECRANKIE

Killiecrankie Visitor Centre

NTS Visitor Centre PH16 5LG
☎ 0844 493 2194
e-mail: information@nts.org.uk
web: www.nts.org.uk
dir: 3m N of Pitlochry on B8079

The visitor centre features an exhibition on the battle of 1689, when the Jacobite army routed the English, although the Jacobite leader, 'Bonnie Dundee', was mortally wounded in the attack. The wooded gorge is a notable beauty spot, admired by Queen Victoria, and there are some splendid walks.

Times Visitor Centre: Open Apr-1 Nov, daily 10-5.30. Site: open all year daily.* Facilities ℗ ⊑ ⊓ (outside) ♿ (partly accessible) (footpath down into the pass is steep with uneven path and steps) toilets for disabled shop ♨

MILNATHORT

Burleigh Castle

KY13 7XZ
web: www.historic-scotland.gov.uk
dir: 0.5m E of Milnathort on A911

The roofless but otherwise complete ruin of a tower house of about 1500, with a section of defensive barmkin wall and a remarkable corner tower with a square cap-house corbelled out. This castle was often visited by James IV.

Times Open summer only. Keys available locally, telephone 01786 45000.* Facilities ⊗ 桌

PERTH

Caithness Glass Factory & Visitor Centre

Inveralmond PH1 3TZ
☎ 01738 492320 📄 01738 492300
e-mail: visitorcentre@caithnessglass.co.uk
web: www.caithnessglass.co.uk
dir: on Perth Western Bypass, A9, at Inveralmond Roundabout

All aspects of paperweight-making can be seen from the purpose-built viewing galleries. Visitors can now enter the glasshouse on a route which enables them to watch the glassmakers closely. There are talks in the glasshouse regularly throughout the day from Monday to Friday. There is also a factory shop, a best shop, children's play area and tourist information centre with internet access.

Times Open all year, Factory shop & restaurant Mon-Sat 9-5, Sun 10-5 (Jan-Feb 12-5). Glassmaking Mon-Sun 9-4.30.* **Facilities** ℗ ⧆ licensed ⌐ (outdoor) ⅙ toilets for disabled shop ⊗

PERTH

Perth Museum & Art Gallery

78 George St PH1 5LB
☎ 01738 632488 📄 01738 443505
e-mail: museum@pkc.gov.uk
web: www.pkc.gov.uk
dir: in town centre, adjacent to Perth Concert Hall

Visit Perth Museum and Art Gallery for a fascinating look into Perthshire throughout the ages. Collections cover silver, glass, art, natural history, archaeology and human history.

Times Open all year, Mon-Sat 10-5, Sun 1-4.30, May-Sep. Closed Xmas-New Year.* **Facilities** ℗ toilets for disabled shop ⊗

PITLOCHRY

Edradour Distillery

PH16 5JP

☎ 01796 472095 📄 01796 472002
e-mail: info@signatoryvintage.com
web: www.edradour.co.uk
dir: 2.5m E of Pitlochry on A924

It was in 1825 that a group of local farmers founded Edradour, naming it after the bubbling burn that runs through it. It is Scotland's smallest distillery and is virtually unchanged since Victorian times. Have a dram of whisky while watching an audio-visual in the malt barn and then take a guided tour through the distillery itself.

Times Open Jan-Feb, Mon-Sat 10-4, Sun 12.4; Mar-Oct, Mon-Sat 9.30-6, Sun 11.30-5; Nov-Dec, Mon-Sat 9.30-5, Sun 12-5. (Last tour 1hr before close, private tours arranged for a fee).* Facilities ℗ 🍽 ♿ (partly accessible) toilets for disabled shop ⊗

PITLOCHRY

Scottish Hydro Electric Visitor Centre, Dam & Fish Pass

PH16 5ND

☎ 01796 473152 📄 01796 473152
dir: off A9, 24m N of Perth

The visitor centre features an exhibition showing how electricity is brought from the power station to the customer, and there is access to the turbine viewing gallery. The salmon ladder viewing chamber allows you to see the fish as they travel upstream to their spawning ground.

Times Open Apr-Oct, Mon-Fri 10-5. Wknd opening Jul, Aug & BHs Facilities ℗ ℗ ♿ (partly accessible) (access to shop only) toilets for disabled shop ⊗

QUEEN'S VIEW

Queen's View Visitor Centre

PH16 5NR

☎ 01350 727284   📠 01350 728635
e-mail: peter.fullarton@forestry.gsi.gov.uk
web: www.forestry.gov.uk
dir: 7m W of Pitlochry on B8019

Queen Victoria admired the view on a visit here in 1866; it is possibly one of the most famous views in Scotland. The area, in the heart of the Tay Forest Park, has a variety of woodlands that visitors can walk or cycle in.

Times Open Apr-Nov, daily 10-6.* Facilities ℗
℗ ☐ ⌂ (outdoor) toilets for disabled shop

PAISLEY

Coats Observatory

High St PA1 2BA

☎ 0141 889 2013   📠 0141 889 9240
e-mail: ram.els@renfrewshire.gov.uk
web: www.renfrewshire.gov.uk
dir: M8 junct 27, follow signs to town centre until Gordon St (A761). Left onto Causeyside St, left onto Stone St then left onto High St

The Observatory, funded by Thomas Coats and designed by John Honeyman, was opened in 1883. It houses a 5 inch telescope under the dome at the top. Weather recording activities have been carried out here continuously since 1884. There is also earthquake-measuring equipment and the Renfrewshire Astronomical Society holds regular meetings here. There are displays on the solar system, earthquakes and the telescope.

Times Open all year, Tue-Sat 10-5, Sun 2-5. Last entry 15 minutes before closing.* Facilities ℗
shop ⊗

PAISLEY

Paisley Museum

High St PA1 2BA

☎ 0141 889 3151 📄 0141 889 9240
e-mail: ram.els@renfrewshire.gov.uk
web: www.renfrewshire.gov.uk
dir: M8 junct 27 (A741), rdbt 2nd exit (A761-town
centre). At traffic lights take left lane towards
Kilbride. Onto Gordon St, right onto Causeyside
St, left onto New St, left onto High St

Pride of place here is given to a world-famous
collection of Paisley shawls. Other collections
illustrate local industrial and natural history,
while the emphasis of the art gallery is on 19th-
century Scottish artists and an important studio
ceramics collection.

Times Open all year, Tue-Sat 10-5, Sun 2-5.
BH 10-5.* Facilities ℗ ♿ (partly accessible)
(level access available through side entrance, lift
gives access to main gallery, Shawl gallery only
available via rear entrance) toilets for disabled
shop ⊗

JEDBURGH

Jedburgh Castle Jail & Museum

Castlegate TD8 6QD

☎ 01835 864750 📄 01835 864750
web: www.scotborders.gov.uk/museums
dir: off A68 towards town centre, follow signs to
top of Castlegate

Relive the harsh realities of prison life in the
19th century with a visit to Jedburgh Castle
Jail, built in the 1820s on the site of the Royal
Burgh's medieval castle. Displays in the cell
blocks recreate the lives of prisoners and staff,
while the Jailer's House explores the history of
the town. A children's activity guide is available,
and there are plenty of hands-on activities for
all the family.

Times Open late Mar-end Oct, Mon-Sat, 10-4.30,
Sun 1-4* Facilities ℗ ℗ ⊼ (outdoor) ♿ (partly
accessible) toilets for disabled shop ⊗

KELSO

Kelso Abbey

☎ 0131 668 8800
web: www.historic-scotland.gov.uk

Founded by David I in 1128 and probably the greatest of the four famous Border abbeys, Kelso became extremely wealthy and acquired extensive lands. In 1545 it served as a fortress when the town was attacked by the Earl of Hertford, but now only fragments of the once-imposing abbey church give any clue to its long history.

Times Open at any reasonable time.* Facilities ⁂

SELKIRK

Halliwells House Museum

Halliwells Close, Market Place TD7 4BC
☎ 01750 20096 📄 01750 23282
e-mail: museums@scotborders.gov.uk
dir: off A7 in town centre

A row of late 18th-century town cottages converted into a museum. Displays recreate the building's former use as an ironmonger's shop and home, and tell the story of the Royal Burgh of Selkirk. The Robson Gallery hosts a programme of contemporary art and craft exhibitions.

Times Open Apr-Sep, Mon-Sat 10-5, Sun 10-12; Jul-Aug, Mon-Sat 10-5.30, Sun 10-12; Oct, Mon-Sat 10-4.* Facilities 🅿 Ⓟ ♿ toilets for disabled shop ⊗

SELKIRK

Sir Walter Scott's Courtroom

Market Place TD7 4BT

☎ 01750 20096 📄 01750 23282

e-mail: museums@scotborders.gov.uk

dir: on A7 in town centre

Built in 1803-4 as a sheriff court and town hall this is where the famous novelist, Sir Walter Scott dispensed justice when he was Sheriff of Selkirkshire from 1804-1832. Displays tell of Scott's time as Sheriff, and of his place as a novelist as well as those of his contemporaries, writer, James Hogg and the explorer, Mungo Park.

Times Open Apr-Sep, Mon-Fri 10-4, Sat 10-2; May-Aug also Sun 10-2; Oct, Mon-Sat 1-4.* Facilities Ⓟ ♿ (partly accessible) (ramp at rear of building) toilets for disabled shop ⊗

HAMILTON

Chatelherault Country Park

Ferniegair ML3 7UE

☎ 01698 426213 📄 01698 427741

e-mail: phyllis.crosbie@southlanarkshire.gov.uk

web: www.southlanarkshire.gov.uk

dir: 2.5km SE of Hamilton on A72 Hamilton-Larkhall/Lanark Clyde Valley tourist route

Designed as a hunting lodge by William Adam in 1732, Chatelherault, built of unusual pink sandstone, has been described as a gem of Scottish architecture. Situated close to the motorway, there is a visitor's centre, shop and adventure playground. Also a herd of white Cadzow cattle.

Times Visitor Centre, open all year, Mon-Sat 10-5, Sun 12-5. House closed all day Fri & Sat.* Facilities Ⓟ ⊑ 🍴 (outdoor) toilets for disabled shop ⊗

HAMILTON

Low Parks Museum

129 Muir St ML3 6BJ

☎ 01698 328232 📠 01698 328412

e-mail: lowparksmuseum@southlanarkshire.gov.uk

web: www.southlanarkshire.gov.uk

dir: off M74 junct 6, by Asda Superstore

The museum tells the story of both South Lanarkshire and The Cameronians (Scottish Rifles). The Cameronians were unique as they were the only Scottish rifle regiment, and the museum details their fascinating history from 1689 to 1968. Housed in the town's oldest building, dating from 1696, the museum also features a restored 18th-century assembly room and exhibitions on Hamilton Palace and The Covenanters.

Times Open all year, daily, Mon-Sat 10-5, Sun 12-5* Facilities 🅿 Ⓟ ♿ toilets for disabled shop ⊗

STIRLING

Mar's Wark

Broad St FK8 1EE

web: www.historic-scotland.gov.uk

A remarkable Renaissance mansion built by the Earl of Mar, Regent for James VI in 1570 and later used as the town workhouse. It was never completed and now the façade can be seen.

Times Open all reasonable times.* Facilities ⊗ 🔖

ROTHESAY

Ardencraig

9 Ardencraig Ln, High Craigmore PA20 9EZ
☎ 01700 504644
e-mail: enquiries@argyll-bute.gov.uk
web: www.argyll-bute.gov.uk
dir: 1m off A844, S of Rothesay

Particular attention has been paid to improving the layout of the garden and introducing rare plants. The greenhouse and walled garden produce plants for floral displays throughout the district. A variety of fish is kept in the ornamental ponds and the aviaries have some interesting birds.

Times Open May-Sep, Mon-Thu 9-4, Fri 9-3.30, Sat-Sun 1-4.30. Facilities ❷ ℗ ⅋ (partly accessible) (75% nursery wheelchair accessible using ramps) toilets for disabled ⊗

MILLPORT

Museum of the Cumbraes

Garrison Grounds KA28 0DG
☎ 01475 531191
e-mail: namuseum@north-ayrshire.gov.uk
web: www.north-ayrshire.gov.uk/museums
dir: Ferry to Millport, from Largs Cal-Mac Terminal. Bus meets each ferry

A small museum which displays the history and life of the Cumbraes. There is also a fine collection of local photographs.

Times Open Etr-Sep, daily from 9 (Sat & Sun from 12).* Facilities ❷ ℗ ⬛⅋ shop ⊗

CARLOWAY

Dun Carloway Broch

☎ 1851 710395
web: www.historic-scotland.gov.uk
dir: 1.5m S of Carloway on A858

Brochs are late-prehistoric circular stone towers, and their origins are mysterious. One of the best examples can be seen at Dun Carloway, where the tower still stands about 30ft high.

Times Open at all reasonable times.*
Facilities ℗ 屪

BIRSAY

Earl's Palace

KW15 1PD
☎ 01856 721205 & & 841815
web: www.historic-scotland.gov.uk
dir: on A966

The gaunt remains of the residence of the 16th-century Earl of Orkney, constructed round a courtyard.

Times Open at all reasonable times.*
Facilities ⊗ 屪

DOUNBY

Click Mill

☎ 01856 841815
web: www.historic-scotland.gov.uk
dir: 2.5m from Dounby on B905

The last surviving horizontal water mill in Orkney, of a type well represented in Shetland and Lewis. The mill is in working condition and visitors should wear sensible footwear.

Times Open at all reasonable times.* Facilities 🏳

FINSTOWN

Stones of Stenness Circle and Henge

☎ 01856 841815
web: www.historic-scotland.gov.uk
dir: 5m NE of Stromness on B9055

Dating back to the second millennium BC, the remains of this stone circle are near the Ring of Brogar - a splendid circle of upright stones surrounded by a ditch.

Times Open at any reasonable time.*
Facilities 🅿 🏳

HARRAY

Corrigall Farm & Kirbuster Museum

KW17 2JR

☎ 01856 771411 & 771268

web: www.orkneyheritage.com

dir: Off A986, main road through parish of Harray to parish of Birsay

The museum consists of two Orkney farmhouses with outbuildings. Kirbuster (Birsay) has the last surviving example of a 'Firehoose' with its central hearth; Corrigall (Harray) represents an improved farmhouse and steading of the late 1800s.

Times Open Mar-Oct, Mon-Sat 10.30-1 & 2-5, Sun 12-5. Facilities ❷ ℗ 卅 (outdoor) ঌ toilets for disabled shop ⊗

KIRKWALL

The Orkney Museum

Broad St KW15 1DH

☎ 01856 87355 ext 2523   📄 01856 871560

e-mail: museum@orkney.gov.uk

web: www.orkney.gov.uk

dir: town centre

One of the finest vernacular town houses in Scotland, this 16th-century building now contains a museum of Orkney history, including the islands' fascinating archaeology and social history.

Times Open all year, Oct-Apr, Mon-Sat 10.30-12.30 & 1.30-5; May-Sep, Mon-Sat 10.30-5. Facilities ℗ ঌ (partly accessible) (5 galleries at ground level, 8 galleries require use of stair lift) toilets for disabled shop ⊗

KIRKWALL

Scapa Flow Visitor Centre & Museum

Lyness, Hoy KW16 3NU
☎ 01856 791300 📄 01856 871560
e-mail: museum@orkney.gov.uk
web: www.orkney.gov.uk
dir: on A964 to Houton, ferry crossing takes 30 mins, visitors centre 2 mins walk from ferry terminal

Also known as the Lyness Interpretation Centre, this fascinating museum is home to a large collection of military equipment used in the defence of the Orkneys during the First and Second World Wars. There are also guns salvaged from the German ships scuppered in WWII. Visitors arrive at the island after a short boat trip from the Orkney mainland.

Times Open all year: Mon-Fri 9-4.30 (mid May-Sep also Sat-Sun 10.30-3.30). Facilities ℗ ☕ & toilets for disabled shop ⊗

STROMNESS

Pier Arts Centre

KW16 3AA
☎ 01856 850209 📄 01856 851462
e-mail: info@pierartscentre.com
web: www.pierartscentre.com

A permanent collection of modern art and sculpture including works by Barbara Hepworth and Ben Nicholson, given to Orkney by the late Margaret Gardiner. These works are housed in a landmark 18th-century building that has served as merchant's offices, a cooperage, stores and private lodgings.

Times Open all year, Mon-Sat 10.30-5, Jul-Sep open Sun 12-4* Facilities ℗ & toilets for disabled shop ⊗

WESTRAY

Noltland Castle

☎ 01856 841815
web: www.historic-scotland.gov.uk
dir: 1m W of Pierowall village

A fine, ruined Z-plan tower, built between 1560 and 1573 but never completed. The tower is remarkable for its large number of gun loops and impressive staircase.

Times Open 11 Jun-Sep, daily 9.30-5.30.*
Facilities ⊗ ▉

LERWICK

Clickimin

ZE1 0QX
☎ 01856 841815
web: www.historic-scotland.gov.uk
dir: 1m SW of Lerwick on A970

The remains of a prehistoric settlement that was fortified at the beginning of the Iron Age with a stone-built fort. The site was occupied for over 1000 years. The remains include a partially demolished broch (round tower) which still stands to a height of 17ft.

Times Open at all reasonable times.* Facilities ▉

LERWICK

Fort Charlotte

ZE1 0JN

☎ 01667 460232

web: www.historic-scotland.gov.uk

dir: in centre of Lerwick

A five-sided artillery fort with bastions projecting from each corner. The walls are high and massive. It was built in 1665 to protect the Sound of Bressay from the Dutch, but taken by them and burned in 1673. It was rebuilt in 1781.

Times Open at all reasonable times. Key available locally.* Facilities 🔖

LERWICK

Shetland Museum

Hay's Dock ZE1 0WP

☎ 01595 695057 📄 01595 696729

e-mail: info@shetlandmuseumandarchives. org.uk

web: www.shetlandmuseumandarchives.org.uk

After a grand re-opening in May 2007, the Museum and Archives sits in a unique dockside setting and is home to 3000 artefacts telling the story of Shetland.

Times Open all year, Jan-Apr & Oct-Dec Mon-Sat 10-5, Sun 12-5; May-Sep Mon-Fri 10-5.30, Sat 10-5, Sun 12-5. Check website for Xmas and New Year. Facilities 🅿 Ⓟ ⛺ 🍴 licensed ♿ toilets for disabled shop ⊗

MOUSA ISLAND

Mousa Broch

☎ 01950 431367
web: www.historic-scotland.gov.uk
dir: accessible by boat from Sandwick

This broch is the best-preserved example of an Iron Age drystone tower in Scotland. The tower is nearly complete and rises to a height of 40ft. The outer and inner walls both contain staircases that may be climbed to the parapet. Boat not available all year. Contact 01950 431367 for more information.

Times Open at all reasonable time.* Facilities 🔖

SCALLOWAY

Scalloway Castle

ZE1 0TP
☎ 01667 460232
web: www.historic-scotland.gov.uk
dir: 6m from Lerwick on A970

The ruins of a castle designed on the medieval two-step plan. The castle was actually built in 1600 by Patrick Stewart, Earl of Orkney. When the Earl, who was renowned for his cruelty, was executed in 1615, the castle fell into disuse.

Times Open at all reasonable time.* Facilities
🔖

BRYNCELLI DDU

Bryn Celli Ddu Burial Chamber

☎ 01443 336000
web: www.cadw.wales.gov.uk
dir: 3m W of Menai Bridge off A4080

Excavated in 1865, and then again in 1925-9, this is a prehistoric circular cairn covering a passage grave with a polygonal chamber.

Times Open all year, access available at all reasonable times, which will normally be 10-4 daily.* Facilities ❷ ⊗ ✛

HOLYHEAD

RSPB Nature Reserve South Stack Cliffs

Plas Nico, South Stack LL65 1YH
☎ 01407 764973
e-mail: south.stack@rspb.org.uk
web: www.rspb.org.uk/reserves/southstack
dir: A5 or A55 to Holyhead follow town centre then follow brown heritage signs

South Stack Cliffs is an expanse of heathland with dramatic sea cliffs and tremendous views. In summer breeding seabirds, including puffins, can be seen from the Information Centre at Ellins Tower where telescopes are provided and staff are on hand to help. There are also large screen televisions displaying live images of the seabirds which staff can control from the information centre to give visitors an amazing 'Big Brother' type view of the breeding seabirds.

Times Open: Information Centre daily, Etr-Sep, 10-5.30. Reserve open daily at all times. Facilities ❷ ⓟ ♿ (partly accessible) (natural surface paths and tracks) toilets for disabled

LLANALLGO

Din Llugwy Ancient Village

☎ 01443 336000
web: www.cadw.wales.gov.uk
dir: 0.75m NW off A5025

The remains of a 4th-century village can be seen here. There are two circular and seven rectangular buildings, still standing up to head height and encircled by a pentagonal stone wall some 4 to 5ft thick.

Times Open all year, access available at all reasonable times, which will normally be 10-4 daily.* Facilities ⊗ ✤

BRIDGEND

Newcastle

☎ 01443 336000
web: www.cadw.wales.gov.uk

The small castle dates back to the 12th century. It is ruined, but a rectangular tower, a richly carved Norman gateway and massive curtain walls enclosing a polygonal courtyard can still be seen.

Times Open all year, access available at all reasonable times, which will normally be 10-4 daily. Key keeper arrangement.* Facilities ℗ ⊗ ✤

COITY

Coity Castle

CF35 6BG

☎ 01443 336000

web: www.cadw.wales.gov.uk

dir: 2m NE of Bridgend, off A4061

A 12th to 16th-century stronghold, with a hall, chapel and the remains of a square keep.

Times Open all year, access available at all reasonable times, which will normally be 10-4 daily. Key keeper arrangement.* Facilities ℗ 🚫 ♿

CARDIFF

National Museum Cardiff

Cathays Park CF10 3NP

☎ 029 2039 7951   📄 029 2057 3321

e-mail: post@museumwales.ac.uk

web: www.museumwales.ac.uk

dir: in Civic Centre. M4 junct 32, A470, 5 mins walk from city centre & 20 mins walk from bus & train station

National Museum Cardiff is home to spectacular collections from Wales and all over the world. The Museum showcases displays of art, archaeology, geology and natural history. The new archaeology gallery, 'Origins in search of early Wales', traces life in Wales from the earliest humans 230,000 years ago. Explore the past through themes such as conflict, power, wealth, family and the future. Discover some of Wales' most famous works of art in the new art galleries, which now include activity stations and touch screens to help bring the paintings to life. There are also changing displays from the collection of Impressionist and Post-Impressionist paintings, including work by Monet, Renoir and Cézanne.

Times Open all year, Tue-Sun 10-5. Closed Mon (ex BHs). Telephone for Xmas opening times. Fees Free admission but charge may be made for some events. Facilities ℗ ℗ 🍴 licensed ♿ toilets for disabled shop 🚫

ST FAGANS

St Fagans: National History Museum

CF5 6XB

☎ 029 2057 3500 📠 029 2057 3490
web: www.museumwales.ac.uk
dir: 4m W of Cardiff on A4232. From M4 exit at
junct 33 and follow brown signs

A stroll around the indoor galleries and 100 acres
of beautiful grounds will give you a fascinating
insight into how people in Wales have lived,
worked and spent their leisure hours since
Celtic times. You can see people practising
the traditional means of earning a living, the
animals they kept and at certain times of year,
the ways in which they celebrated the seasons.

Times Open all year daily, 10-5. (Closed 24-26
Dec). Fees Free. Charge may apply to some
events. Facilities ℗ ⬚ ¶◎ licensed ⋔ (outdoor)
♿ (partly accessible) (wheelchair access
possible to most parts) toilets for disabled shop
⊗

ABERGWILI

Carmarthenshire County Museum

SA31 2JG

☎ 01267 228696 📠 01267 223830
e-mail: museums@carmarthenshire.gov.uk
web: www.carmarthenshire.gov.uk/
dir: 2m E of Carmarthen, just off A40, at
Abergwili rdbt

Housed in the old palace of the Bishop of St
David's and set in seven acres of grounds, the
museum offers a wide range of local subjects
to explore, from geology and prehistory to butter
making, Welsh furniture and folk art. Temporary
exhibitions are held.

Times Open all year, Mon-Sat 10-4.30. Closed
Xmas-New Year.* Facilities ℗ ℗ ⬚ ⋔
(outdoor) ♿ toilets for disabled shop ⊗

DRYSLWYN

Dryslwyn Castle

☎ 029 2050 0200
web: www.cadw.wales.gov.uk
dir: on B4279

The ruined 13th-century castle was a stronghold of the native Welsh. It stands on a lofty mound, and was important in the struggles between English and Welsh. It is gradually being uncovered by excavation.

Times Open-entrance by arrangement with Dryslwyn Farm.* Facilities ℗ ⊗ ⊕

LLANSTEFFAN

Llansteffan Castle

☎ 01443 336000
web: www.cadw.wales.gov.uk
dir: off B4312

The ruins of this 11th to 13th-century stronghold stand majestically on the west side of the Towy estuary.

Times Open all year, access available at all reasonable times, which will normally be 10-4 daily. Key keeper arrangement.* Facilities ⊗ ⊕

LLANRWST

Gwydyr Uchaf Chapel

☎ 01492 640578
web: www.cadw.wales.gov.uk
dir: 0.5m SW off B5106

Built in the 17th century by Sir John Wynn of
Gwydir Castle, the chapel is noted for its painted
ceiling and wonderfully varied woodwork.

Times Open all year, access available at all
reasonable times, which will normally be 10-4
daily. Key keeper arrangement.* Facilities ℗
⊗ ♿ ⊕

EWLOE

Ewloe Castle

☎ 01443 336000
web: www.cadw.wales.gov.uk
dir: 1m NW of village on B5125

Standing in Ewloe Wood are the remains of
Ewloe Castle. It was a native Welsh castle, and
Henry II was defeated nearby in 1157. Part of the
Welsh Tower in the upper ward still stands to its
original height, and there is a well in the lower
ward. Remnants of walls and another tower can
also be seen.

Times Open all year, access available at all
reasonable times, which will normally be 10-4
daily.* Facilities ⊗ ⊕

FLINT

Flint Castle

CH6 5PH
☎ 01443 336000
web: www.cadw.wales.gov.uk
dir: NE side of Flint

The castle was started by Edward I in 1277 and overlooks the River Dee. It is exceptional for its great tower, or Donjon, which is separated by a moat. Other buildings would have stood in the inner bailey, of which parts of the walls and corner towers remain.

Times Open all year, access available at all reasonable times, which will normally be 10-4 daily. Key keeper arrangement.* Facilities ℗ ⊗ ♿

HOLYWELL

Basingwerk Abbey

Greenfield Valley Heritage Pk, Greenfield
CH8 7GH
☎ 01443 336000
web: www.cadw.wales.gov.uk
dir: just S of A458

The abbey was founded around 1131 by Ranulf de Gernon, Earl of Chester. The first stone church dates from the beginning of the 13th century. The last abbot surrendered the house to the crown in 1536. The Abbey is close to the Heritage Park Visitor Centre and access to the Museum and Farm Complex at Greenfield Valley.

Times Open all year, access available at all reasonable times, which will normally be 10-4 daily.* Facilities ℗ ⚫ licensed ⊓ toilets for disabled shop ⊗ ♿

CAERNARFON

Segontium Roman Museum

Beddgelert Rd LL55 2LN

☎ 01286 675625 📠 01286 678416

e-mail: info@segontium.org.uk

web: www.segontium.org.uk

dir: on A4085 to Beddgelert approx 1m from Caernarfon

Segontium Roman Museum tells the story of the conquest and occupation of Wales by the Romans and displays the finds from the auxiliary fort of Segontium, one of the most famous in Britain. You can combine a visit to the museum with exploration of the site of the Roman Fort, which is in the care of Cadw: Welsh Historic Monuments. The exciting discoveries displayed at the museum vividly portray the daily life of the soldiers stationed in this most westerly outpost of the Roman Empire.

Times Open all year, Tue-Sun 12.30-4. Closed Mon except BH* Facilities ℗ shop ⊗

CYMER ABBEY

Cymer Abbey

☎ 01443 336000

web: www.cadw.wales.gov.uk

dir: 2m NW of Dolgellau on A494

The abbey was built for the Cistercians in the 13th century. It was never very large, and does not seem to have been finished. The church is the best-preserved building, with ranges of windows and arcades still to be seen. The other buildings have been plundered for stone, but low outlines remain.

Times Open all year, access available at all reasonable times, which will normally be 10-4 daily. Key keeper arrangement.* Facilities ℗ ⊗ ⊕

Dolbadarn Castle

LL55 4UD

☎ 01443 336000

web: www.cadw.wales.gov.uk

dir: A4086

Built by Llywelyn the Great in the early 13th century, this Welsh castle overlooks Llyn Padarn in the Llanberis Pass.

Times Open all year, access available at all reasonable times, which will normally be 10-4 daily.* Facilities ❷ ❽ ✛

Castell-y-Bere

☎ 01443 336000

web: www.cadw.wales.gov.uk

dir: off B4405

The castle was begun around 1221 by Prince Llewelyn ap Iorwerth of Gwynedd to guard the southern flank of his principality. It is typically Welsh in design with its D-shaped towers. Although a little off the beaten track, the castle lies in a spectacular setting, overshadowed by the Cader Idris range.

Times Open all year, access available at all reasonable times, which will normally be 10-4 daily.* Facilities ❽ ✛

LLANGYBI

St Cybi's Well

☎ 01443 336000
web: www.cadw.wales.gov.uk
dir: off B4354

Cybi was a sixth-century Cornish saint, known as a healer of the sick, and St Cybi's Well (or Ffynnon Gybi) has been famous for its curative properties through the centuries. The corbelled beehive vaulting inside the roofless stone structure is Irish in style and unique in Wales.

Times Open all year, access available at all reasonable times, which will normally be 10-4 daily.* Facilities ⊗ ⊕

PENARTH FAWR

Penarth Fawr

☎ 01443 336000
web: www.cadw.wales.gov.uk
dir: 3.5m NE of Pwllheli off A497

The hall, buttery and screen are preserved in this house which was probably built in the 15th century.

Times Open all year, access available at all reasonable times, which will normally be 10-4 daily.* Facilities ⊗ ⊕

MERTHYR TYDFIL

Cyfarthfa Castle Museum & Art Gallery

Cyfarthfa Park CF47 8RE
☎ 01685 723112   🖷 01685 723112
e-mail: museum@merthyr.gov.uk
web: www.museums.merthyr.gov.uk
dir: off A470, N towards Brecon, follow brown heritage signs

Set in wooded parkland beside a beautiful lake, this imposing Gothic mansion now houses a superb museum and art gallery. Providing a fascinating glimpse into 3,000 years of history, the museum displays wonderful collections of fine art, social history and objects from around the world in a Regency setting.

Times Open Apr-Sep, daily, 10-5.30 (last admission 5); Oct-Mar, Tue-Fri 10-4, Sat-Sun 12-4. Closed between Xmas & New Year. Facilities 🅿 🅟 ⬚🭩 (outdoor) ♿ toilets for disabled shop ⊗

CAERWENT

Caerwent Roman Town

☎ 01443 336000
web: www.cadw.wales.gov.uk
dir: just off A48

A complete circuit of the town wall of 'Venta Silurum', together with excavated areas of houses, shops and a temple.

Times Open - access throughout the year. There is a facilitator on site each Tue. For group bookings Tel: (01633) 430576.* Facilities ⊗ ⊕

GROSMONT

Grosmont Castle

☎ 01981 240301
web: www.cadw.wales.gov.uk
dir: on B4347

Grosmont is one of the 'trilateral' castles of Hubert de Burgh (see also Skenfrith and White Castle). It stands on a mound with a dry moat, and the considerable remains of its 13th-century great hall can be seen. Three towers once guarded the curtain wall, and the western one is well preserved.

Times Open all year, access available at all reasonable times, which will normally be 10-4 daily.* Facilities ⊗ ⊕

LLANTHONY

Llanthony Priory

☎ 01443 336000
web: www.cadw.wales.gov.uk

William de Lacey discovered the remains of a hermitage dedicated to St David. By 1108 a church had been consecrated on the site and just over a decade later the priory was complete. After the priory was brought to a state of siege in an uprising, Hugh de Lacey provided the funds for a new church, and it is this that makes the picturesque ruin seen today. Visitors can still make out the west towers, north nave arcade and south transept.

Times Open all year, access available at all reasonable times, which will normally be 10-4 daily.* Facilities ℗ toilets for disabled ⊗ ⊕

LLANTILIO CROSSENNY

Hen Gwrt

☎ 01443 336000
web: www.cadw.wales.gov.uk
dir: off B4233

The rectangular enclosure of the former medieval house, still surrounded by a moat.

Times Open all year, access available at all reasonable times, which will normally be 10-4 daily.* Facilities ⊗ 🚾 ⊕

MONMOUTH

The Nelson Museum & Local History Centre

New Market Hall, Priory St NP25 3XA
☎ 01600 710630
e-mail: nelsonmuseum@monmouthshire.gov.uk
dir: in town centre

One of the world's major collections of Admiral Nelson-related items, including original letters, glass, china, silver, medals, books, models, prints and Nelson's fighting sword feature here. The local history displays deal with Monmouth's past as a fortress market town, and include a section on the co-founder of the Rolls Royce company, Charles Stewart Rolls, who was also a pioneer balloonist, aviator and, of course, motorist. A major exhibition on C S Rolls and his family will take place between January and August 2010. 12 July 2010 commemorates the centenary of the death of C S Rolls.

Times Open all year, Mar-Oct, Mon-Sat & BH 11-1 & 2-5, Sun 2-5; Nov-Feb, Mon-Sat 11-1 & 2-4, Sun 2-4. Facilities Ⓟ ♿ (partly accessible) (mezzanine display area accessible only by stairs - 25% of whole museum display area) toilets for disabled shop ⊗

SKENFRITH

Skenfrith Castle

☎ 01443 336000
web: www.cadw.wales.gov.uk
dir: on B4521

This 13th-century castle has a round keep set inside an imposing towered curtain wall. Hubert de Burgh built it as one of three 'trilateral' castles to defend the Welsh Marches.

Times Open all year, access available at all reasonable times, which will normally be 10-4 daily. Key keeper arrangement.* Facilities ⓟ ⊗ ✥ ⛵

CRYNANT

Cefn Coed Colliery Museum

SA10 8SN
☎ 01639 750556 📄 01639 750556
e-mail: colliery@btconnect.com
web: www.neath-porttalbot.gov.uk
dir: 1m S of Crynant, on A4109

The museum is on the site of a former working colliery, and tells the story of mining in the Dulais Valley. A steam-winding engine has been kept and is now operated by electricity, and there is also a simulated underground mining gallery, boilerhouse, compressor house, and exhibition area. Outdoor exhibits include a stationary colliery locomotive. Exhibitions relating to the coal mining industry are held on a regular basis. The museum is now home to the Dulais Valley Historical Model Railway Society who, with the help from the Heritage Lottery Fund have created an ever increasing layout depicting the Neath-Brecon railway through the valley. 2010 is the 30th anniversary of the museum.

Times Open Apr-Oct, daily 10.30-5; Nov-Mar, groups welcome by prior arrangement.* Facilities ⓟ � (outdoor) ♿ (partly accessible) (access to exhibition areas, but not to underground gallery) toilets for disabled shop

NEATH

Neath Abbey

SA10 7DW
☎ 01443 336000
web: www.cadw.wales.gov.uk
dir: 1m W off A465

These ruins were originally a Cistercian abbey founded in 1130 by Richard de Grainville.

Times Open all year, access available at all reasonable times, which will normally be 10-4 daily. Key keeper arrangement.* Facilities ℗ ⊗ ⊕

CAERLEON

Caerleon Roman Baths

NP18 1AE
☎ 01663 422518
web: www.cadw.wales.gov.uk
dir: on B4236

Caerleon was an important Roman military base, with accommodation for thousands of men. The foundations of barrack lines and parts of the ramparts can be seen, with remains of the cookhouse, latrines and baths. The amphitheatre nearby is one of the best examples in Britain.

Times Open all year, Apr-Oct, daily 9.30-5; Nov-Mar, Mon-Sat, 9.30-5, Sun 11-4.* Facilities ℗ shop ⊗ ⊕

CAERLEON

National Roman Legion Museum

High St NP18 1AE

☎ 01633 423134   🖷 01633 422869

e-mail: roman@museumwales.ac.uk

web: www.museumwales.ac.uk

dir: close to Newport, 20 min from M4, follow signs from Cardiff & Bristol

The museum illustrates the history of Roman Caerleon and the daily life of its garrison. On display are arms, armour and equipment, with a collection of engraved gemstones, a labyrinth mosaic and finds from the legionary base at Usk. Please telephone for details of children's holiday activities.

Times Open all year: Mon-Sat 10-5, Sun 2-5.*
Facilities ℗ toilets for disabled shop ⊗

FISHGUARD

OceanLab

The Parrog, Goodwick SA64 0DE

☎ 01348 874737   🖷 01348 872528

e-mail: fishguardharbour.tic@pembrokeshire.gov.uk

web: www.ocean-lab.co.uk

dir: A40 to Fishguard, turn at by-pass, follow signs for Stenaline ferry terminal, pass 2 garages, turn right at rdbt & follow signs to attraction

Overlooking the Pembrokeshire coastline, OceanLab is a multifunctional centre, which aims to provide a fun-filled experience for the family. There is also a hands-on ocean quest exhibition, a soft play area and a cybercafé. An exhibition is centred around 'Ollie the Octopus's Garden', with hands-on displays and activities.

Times Open Apr-Oct, 9.30-5 (6 wk summer hols 9.30-6); Nov-Mar 10-4. Fees Free admission. £1 soft play under 5's, £2 cyber cafe for 30 mins.
Facilities ℗ ℗ � (outdoor) ♿ toilets for disabled shop ⊗

LLAWHADEN

Llawhaden Castle

☎ 01443 336000
web: www.cadw.wales.gov.uk
dir: off A40, 3m NW of Narberth

The castle was first built in the 12th century to protect the possessions of the Bishops of St David's. The 13th and 14th-century remains of the bishops' hall, kitchen, bakehouse and other buildings can be seen, all surrounded by a deep moat.

Times Open all year, access available at all reasonable times, which will normally be 10-4 daily. Key keeper arrangement.* Facilities ⊗ ⊕

NEWPORT

Pentre Ifan Burial Chamber

☎ 01443 336000
web: www.cadw.wales.gov.uk
dir: 3m SE from B4329 or A487

Found to be part of a vanished long barrow when excavated in 1936-37, the remains of this chamber include the capstone, three uprights and a circular forecourt.

Times Open all year, access available at all reasonable times, which will normally be 10-4 daily.* Facilities ⊗ ⊕

MACHYNLLETH

Corris Craft Centre

Corris SY20 9RF
☎ 01654 761584 📄 01654 761575
e-mail: info@corriscraftcentre.co.uk
web: www.corriscraftcentre.co.uk
dir: on main A487 rd between Machynlleth &
Dolgellau

A large collection of workshops where visitors
can meet the craftspeople and see them at work
every day. The range of crafts include glassware,
leatherwork, pottery, jewellery, traditional wooden
toys and candles. A perfect place to find unusual
items for the home and garden. Drop in for
pottery painting and candle-dipping.

Times Open daily Mar-Nov. From Nov-Mar many
workshops open please call to check dates and
times. Facilities 🅿 ⛻ 㞧 (outdoor) ♿ (partly
accessible) (full access to craft units and cafe at
the craft centre) toilets for disabled shop ⊗

MONTGOMERY

Montgomery Castle

☎ 01443 336000
web: www.cadw.wales.gov.uk

Initially an earth and timber structure
guarding an important ford in the River Severn,
Montgomery was considered a 'suitable spot
for the erection of an impregnable castle' in the
1220s. Building and modifications continued
until 1251-53, but the final conquest of Wales by
Edward I meant the castle lost much of its role.

Times Open all year, access available at all
reasonable times, which will normally be 10-4
daily.* Facilities ⊗ ✛

SWANSEA

Swansea Museum

Victoria Rd, Maritime Quarter SA1 1SN
☎ 01792 653763 📄 01792 652585
e-mail: swansea.museum@swansea.gov.uk
web: www.swanseaheritage.net
dir: M4 junct 42, on main road into city centre, just past Sainsurys on left

This is the oldest museum in Wales, showing the history of Swansea from the earliest times until today. The museum has a Tramshed and floating boats to explore (summer only). There is a continuous programme of temporary exhibitions and events all year around. The collections centre is nearby which is open to the public every Wednesday.

Times Open all year, Tue-Sun 10-5 (last admission 4.45). Closed Mon except BH Mon, 25-26 Dec & 1 Jan. Facilities 🅿 🅟 🍴 (outdoor) ♿ (partly accessible) (lower floor/gallery accessible) toilets for disabled shop ⊗

BLAENAVON

Big Pit National Coal Museum

NP4 9XP
☎ 01495 790311 📄 01495 792618
e-mail: post@museumwales.ac.uk
web: www.museumwales.ac.uk
dir: M4 junct 25/26, follow signs on A4042 & A4043 to Pontypool & Blaenavon. Signed off A465

The Real Underground Experience, Big Pit is the UK's leading mining museum. It is a real colliery and was the place of work for hundreds of men, woman and children for over 200 years. A daily struggle to extract the precious mineral that stoked furnaces and lit household fires across the world.

Times Open all year 9.30-5. Please call for underground guided tour availability*
Facilities 🅿 ⊑ ♿ (partly accessible) toilets for disabled shop ⊗

BLAENAVON

Blaenavon Ironworks

North St NP4 9RN

☎ 01495 792615

web: www.cadw.wales.gov.uk

The Blaenavon Ironworks were a milestone in the history of the Industrial Revolution. Constructed in 1788-99, they were the first purpose-built, multi-furnace ironworks in Wales. By 1796, Blaenavon was the second largest ironworks in Wales, eventually closing down in 1904.

Times Open all year, Apr-Oct, daily 10-5; Nov-Mar, Fri-Sat 9.30-4, Sun 11-4.* Facilities **P**
⊗ ✣

OGMORE

Ogmore Castle

☎ 01443 336000

web: www.cadw.wales.gov.uk

dir: 2.5m SW of Bridgend, on B4524

Standing on the River Ogmore, the west wall of this castle is 40ft high. A hooded fireplace is preserved in the 12th-century, three-storey keep and a dry moat surrounds the inner ward.

Times Open all year, access available at all reasonable times, which will normally be 10-4 daily. Key keeper arrangement.* Facilities **P**
⊗ ✣

ST HILARY

Old Beaupre Castle

☎ 01443 336000
web: www.cadw.wales.gov.uk
dir: 1m SW, off A48

This ruined manor house was rebuilt during the 16th century. Its most notable features are an Italianate gatehouse and porch. The porch is an unusual three-storeyed structure.

Times Open all year, access available at all reasonable times, which will normally be 10-4 daily. Key keeper arrangement.* Facilities Ⓟ
⊗ ✥

ANTRIM

Antrim Round Tower

BT41 1BJ
☎ 028 9023 5000   🖹 028 9031 0288
web: www.ehsni.gov.uk
dir: N of town

Antrim round tower stands among lawns and trees but it was once surrounded by monastic buildings. Antrim was an important early monastery, probably a 6th-century foundation, closely linked with Bangor.

Times Open all year.* Facilities Ⓟ

BALLYCASTLE

Bonamargy Friary

☎ 028 9023 5000   📄 028 9031 0288
web: www.ehsni.gov.uk
dir: E of town, at golf course

Founded by Rory MacQuillan around 1500 and later passed on to the MacDonnells, Earls of Antrim, there are still remains of the friary gatehouse, church and cloister for visitors to see.

Times Open all year.* Facilities 🅿 🚏

BALLYLUMFORD

Ballylumford Dolmen

☎ 028 9023 5000   📄 028 9031 0288
web: www.ehsni.gov.uk
dir: on B90 on NW tip of Island Magee

Incorporated in the front garden of a house in Ballylumford Road are the remains of this huge 4-5,000-year-old single-chamber Neolithic tomb, also known as the Druid's Altar.

Times Open all year.*

BALLYMENA

Ecos Visitor & Conference Centre

Ecos Centre, Kernohams Ln, Broughshane Rd
BT43 7QA

☎ 028 2566 4400   📄 028 2563 8984
e-mail: www.ballymena.gov.uk/ecos
web: www.ballymena.gov.uk/ecos
dir: follow signs from M2 bypass at Ballymena

Plenty of fun and adventure for all the family
with duck feeding, toy tractors and sand pit. The
centre hosts two interactive galleries, one on
sustainability and one on biodiversity, and you
can stroll through the willow tunnel and enjoy
the play park.

Times Open Etr-Oct, Mon-Fri 9-5; Jun-Aug, Sat-
Sun 12-5 (last admission 4). Facilities 🅿 ⛾ 🎪
(outdoor) ♿ toilets for disabled shop ⊗

BALLYMENA

Harryville Motte

☎ 028 9023 5000   📄 028 9031 0288
web: www.ehsni.gov.uk
dir: N bank of River Braid

On a ridge to the south of the town, this Norman
fort, with its 40ft-high motte and rectangular
bailey, is one of the finest examples of Norman
earthworks left in Northern Ireland.

Times Open all year.* Facilities 🅿 🚐

CARRICKFERGUS

Town Walls

☎ 028 9023 5000 📄 028 9031 0288
web: www.ehsni.gov.uk

Lord Deputy Sir Arthur Chichester enclosed
Carrickfergus with stone walls from 1611
onwards and more than half the circuit is still
visible, often to its full height of 4 metres to the
wall walk.

Times Visible at all times.* Facilities **P**

CHURCHTOWN

Cranfield Church

☎ 028 9023 5000 📄 028 9031 0288
web: www.ehsni.gov.uk
dir: 3.75m SW of Randalstown

This small medieval church is situated on the
shores of Lough Neagh. Beside it is a famous
holy well.

Times Open all year.* Facilities **P** 🪑 🚫

LARNE

Olderfleet Castle

☎ 028 9023 5000 📄 028 9031 0288
web: www.ehsni.gov.uk

A 16th-century tower house, the last surviving of three which defended Larne.

Times Open at all times.*

LISBURN

Duneight Motte and Bailey

☎ 028 9023 5000 📄 028 9031 0288
web: www.ehsni.gov.uk
dir: 2.3m S beside Ravernet River

Impressive Anglo-Norman earthwork castle with high mound-embanked enclosure, making use of the defences of an earlier pre-Norman fort.

Times Open all year.*

LISBURN

Irish Linen Centre & Lisburn Museum

Market Square BT28 1AG
☎ 028 9266 3377 🖹 028 9267 2624
e-mail: irishlinencentre@lisburn.gov.uk
web: www.lisburncity.gov.uk
dir: Signed both in and outside town centre. Follow tourist signs from M1

The centre tells the story of the Irish linen industry past and present. The recreation of individual factory scenes brings the past to life and a series of imaginative hands-on activities describe the linen manufacturing processes. The Museum has a range of temporary exhibitions of local interest.

Times Open all year, Mon-Sat, 9.30-5.*
Facilities ℗ ☐ ♿ toilets for disabled shop ⊗

TEMPLEPATRICK

Templetown Mausoleum

BT39
web: www.ntni.org.uk
dir: in Castle Upton graveyard on A6, Belfast-Antrim road

Situated in the graveyard of Castle Upton, this family mausoleum is in the shape of a triumphal arch and was designed by Robert Adam.

Times Open daily during daylight hours.*
Facilities ℗ ℗ 🚗♿

ARMAGH

Armagh County Museum

The Mall East BT61 9BE

☎ 028 3752 3070   📄 028 3752 2631

e-mail: acm.info@nmni.com

web: www.magni.org.uk

dir: in city centre

Housed in a 19th-century schoolhouse, this museum contains an art gallery and library, as well as a collection of local folkcrafts and natural history. Special events are planned thoughout the year.

Times Open all year, Mon-Fri 10-5, Sat 10-1 & 2-5. Facilities ℗ ♿ toilets for disabled shop ⊗

ARMAGH

Armagh Friary

☎ 028 9023 5000   📄 028 9031 0288

web: www.ehsni.gov.uk

dir: SE edge of town

Situated just inside the gates of the former Archbishop's Palace are the remains of the longest friary church in Ireland (163ft). The friary was established in 1263 by Archbishop O'Scanail and destroyed by Shane O'Neill in the middle of the 16th century to prevent it being garrisoned by Elizabethan soldiers.

Times Open all year.* Facilities ℗

CAMLOUGH

Killevy Churches

☎ 028 9023 5000 📄 028 9031 0288
web: www.ehsni.gov.uk
dir: 3m S lower eastern slopes of Slieve Gullion

The ruins of the two churches (10th and 13th-century) stand back to back, at the foot of Slieve Gullion sharing a common wall, but with no way through from one to the other. The churches stand on the site of an important nunnery founded by St Monenna in the 5th century. A huge granite slab in the graveyard supposedly marks the founder's grave. A holy well can be reached by climbing the path north of the graveyard. The nunnery was in use until the Dissolution in 1542.

Times Open all year.*

JONESBOROUGH

Kilnasaggart Inscribed Stone

☎ 028 9023 5000 📄 028 9031 0288
web: www.ehsni.gov.uk
dir: 1.25m S

A granite pillar stone dating back to 8th century, with numerous crosses and a long Irish inscription carved on it.

Times Open all year.*

NEWRY

Moyry Castle

☎ 028 9023 5000   📄 028 9031 0288
web: www.ehsni.gov.uk
dir: 7.5m S

This tall, three-storey keep was built by Lord
Mountjoy, Queen Elizabeth's deputy, in 1601, its
purpose to secure the Gap of the North which was
the main route into Ulster.

Times Open all year*

TYNAN

Village Cross

☎ 028 9023 5000   📄 028 9031 0288
web: www.ehsni.gov.uk

A carved High Cross, 11ft tall, which lay broken
in two pieces for many years, but was skilfully
mended in 1844.

Times Open all year* Facilities 🅿

BELFAST

Giant's Ring

☎ 028 9023 5000   ▤ 028 9031 0288
web: www.ehsni.gov.uk
dir: 0.75m S of Shaws Bridge

Circular, Bronze-age enclosure nearly 200 feet
in diameter similar in style to Stonehenge, with
a stone chambered grave in the centre and
bordered by banks 20 feet wide and 12 feet high.
Very little is known for certain about this site,
except that it was used for ritual burial.

Times Open all times.* Facilities ℗

BELFAST

Ulster Museum

Botanic Gardens BT9 5AB
☎ 028 9038 3000   ▤ 028 9038 3003
e-mail: uminfo@nmni.com
web: www.nmni.com
dir: 1m S of city centre on Stranmillis road

The Ulster Museum is the perfect place to explore
the arts, ancient and modern history, and the
nature of Ireland. Art displays change regularly
but always include a rich variety of Irish and
international paintings, drawings and sculpture,
along with ceramics, glass and costume. The
history galleries tell the story of the north of
Ireland from the Ice Age to the present day. The
natural environment is explored in the Habitas
galleries.

Times Due to open Oct 2009 after major
redevelopment. Please phone or check website
for further details.* Facilities ℗ ☕ toilets for
disabled shop ⊗

BALLYWALTER

Grey Abbey

☎ 028 9054 6552
web: www.ehsni.gov.uk
dir: on E edge of village

Founded in 1193 by Affreca, daughter of the King of the Isle of Man, these extensive ruins of a Cistercian abbey, sitting in lovely sheltered parkland, are among the best preserved in Northern Ireland. The chancel, with its tall lancet windows, magnificent west doorway and an effigy tomb - believed to be Affreca's - in the north wall, are particularly interesting. The abbey was burned down in 1572, and then re-used as a parish church. There are many 17th and 18th-century memorials to be seen in the church ruins, which occupy a pleasant garden setting. The abbey now has a beautiful medieval herb garden, with over 50 varieties of plants, and a visitors' centre.

Times Open Apr-Sep; Tue-Sat 9-6, Sun 2-6; Oct-Mar, wknds 10-4.* Facilities ❷ toilets for disabled

CASTLEWELLAN

Drumena Cashel

☎ 028 9023 5000   📄 028 9031 0288
web: www.ehsni.gov.uk
dir: 2.25m SW

There are many stone ring forts in Northern Ireland, but few so well preserved as Drumena. Dating back to early Christian times, the fort is 30 metre in diameter and has an 11 metre accessible underground stone-built passage, probably used as a refuge and for storage.

Times Open all times*

DOWNPATRICK

Down County Museum

The Mall, County Down, Northern Ireland
BT30 6AH

☎ 028 4461 5218   📄 028 4461 5590
e-mail: museum@downdc.gov.uk
web: www.downcountymuseum.com
dir: on entry to town follow brown signs to
museum

The museum is located in the restored buildings
of the 18th-century county gaol. In addition to
restored cells that tell the stories of some of the
prisoners, there are exhibitions on the history of
County Down. Plus temporary exhibits, events,
tea-room and shop.

Times Open all year, Mon-Fri 10-5, wknds 1-5*
Facilities Ⓟ ⍾ ⼍ (outdoor) toilets for disabled
shop ⊗

DOWNPATRICK

Loughinisland Churches

☎ 028 9023 5000   📄 028 9031 0288
web: www.ehsni.gov.uk
dir: 4m W

This remarkable group of three ancient churches
stands on an island in the lough, accessible by
a causeway. The middle church is the oldest,
probably dating back to the 13th century, with a
draw-bar hole to secure the door. The large North
church was built in the 15th century, possibly to
replace the middle church and continued in use
until 1720. The smallest and most recent church
is the South (MacCartan's) church.

Times Open all times* Facilities Ⓟ ⍾

DOWNPATRICK

Mound of Down

☎ 028 9023 5000 ▤ 028 9031 0288
web: www.ehsni.gov.uk
dir: on Quoile Marshes, from Mount Crescent

A hill fort from the Early Christian period, conquered by Anglo-Norman troops in 1177, who then built an earthwork castle on top. This mound in the marshes, beside the River Quoile, was the first town before the present Downpatrick.

Times Open all times* Facilities ℗

DOWNPATRICK

Struell Wells

☎ 028 9023 5000 ▤ 028 9031 0288
web: www.ehsni.gov.uk
dir: 1.5m E

Pilgrims come to collect the healing waters from these holy drinking and eye wells which are fed by a swift underground stream. Nearby are the ruins of an 18th-century church, and, even more interesting, single-sex bath-houses. The men's bath-house is roofed, has an anteroom and a sunken bath, while the ladies' is smaller and roofless.

Times Open all times* Facilities ℗ ♿

DROMARA

Legananny Dolmen

☎ 028 9023 5000   🖹 028 9031 0288
web: www.ehsni.gov.uk
dir: 4m S

Theatrically situated on the slopes of Slieve Croob, this tripod dolmen with its three tall uprights and huge capstone is the most graceful of Northern Ireland's Stone Age monuments. There are views to the Mourne Mountains.

Times Open at all times* Facilities 🚾

HILLSBOROUGH

Hillsborough Fort

☎ 028 9268 3285   🖹 028 9031 0288
web: www.ehsni.gov.uk

On a site that dates back to early Christian times, the existing fort was built in 1650 by Colonel Arthur Hill to command a view of the road from Dublin to Carrickfergus. The building was ornamented in the 18th century. It is set in a forest park with a lake and pleasant walks.

Times Open all year; summer, Mon-Sat 10-7, Sun 2-7; winter, Mon-Sat 10-4, Sun 2-4* Facilities ℗ 🪑

KILLINCHY

Sketrick Castle

☎ 028 9023 5000 ▤ 028 9031 0288
web: www.ehsni.gov.uk
dir: 3m E on W tip of Sketrick Islands

A badly ruined tall tower house, probably 15th century. The ground floor rooms include a boat bay and prison. An underground passage leads from the north-east of the bawn to a freshwater spring.

Times Open at all times.* Facilities ℗ ㅠ

NEWCASTLE

Dundrum Castle

☎ 028 9054 6518
web: www.ehsni.gov.uk
dir: 4m N

This medieval castle, one of the finest in Ireland, was built in 1777 by John De Courcy in a strategic position overlooking Dundrum Bay, a position which offers visitors fine views over the sea and to the Mourne Mountains. The castle was captured by King John in 1210 and was badly damaged by Cromwellian troops in 1652. Still an impressive ruin, it shows a massive round keep with walls 16 miles high and 2 miles thick, surrounded by a curtain wall, and a gatehouse which dates from the 13th century.

Times Open Apr-Sep, Tue-Sat 10-7, Sun 2-7; Oct-Mar, wknds, Sat 10-4, Sun 2-4.* Facilities ℗ ㅠ toilets for disabled

NEWCASTLE

Maghera Church

☎ 028 9023 5000   📄 028 9031 0288
web: www.ehsni.gov.uk
dir: 2m NNW

The stump of a round tower, blown down in a storm in the early 18th century, survives from the early monastery, with a ruined 13th-century church nearby.

Times Open all year.* Facilities **P**

NEWTOWNARDS

Scrabo Tower

Scrabo Country Park, 203A Scrabo Rd
BT23 4SJ
☎ 028 9181 1491   📄 028 9182 0695
web: www.ehsni.gov.uk
dir: 1m W

The 135 foot high Scrabo Tower, one of Northern Ireland's best-known landmarks, dominates the landscape of North Down and is also the centre of a country park around the slopes of Scrabo Hill. The Tower provides a fascinating series of interpretative displays about the surrounding countryside and the viewing platform boasts spectacular views over Strangford Lough and County Down. The park provides walks through fine beech and hazel woodlands and the unique sandstone quarries display evidence of volcanic activity as well as being breeding sites for peregrine falcons.

Times Open late Mar-mid Sep, Sat-Thu 10.30-6.*
Facilities **P** ⊼ toilets for disabled shop ⊗

STRANGFORD

Strangford Castle

☎ 028 9023 5000 🖹 028 9031 0288
web: www.ehsni.gov.uk

A three-storey tower house built in the 16th century, overlooking the small double harbour of Strangford.

Times Open all reasonable times.* Facilities ⊗

DERRYGONNELLY

Tully Castle

☎ 028 9054 6552
web: www.ehsni.gov.uk
dir: 3m N, on W shore of Lower Lough Erne

Extensive ruins of a Scottish-style stronghouse with enclosing bawn overlooking Lough Erne. Built by Sir John Hume in the early 1600s, the castle was destroyed, and most of the occupants slaughtered, by the Maguires in the 1641 Rising. There is a replica of a 17th-century garden in the bawn.

Times Open Etr-Sep, 10-6.* Facilities ❶ ⊼ ⊗

ENNISKILLEN

Monea Castle

☎ 028 9023 5000   🖹 028 9031 0288
web: www.ehsni.gov.uk
dir: 6m NW

A fine example of a plantation castle still with much of its enclosing bawn wall intact, built around 1618. Of particular interest is the castle's stone corbelling - the Scottish method of giving additional support to turrets.

Times Open at any reasonable time.*
Facilities **℗**

LISNASKEA

Castle Balfour

☎ 028 9023 5000   🖹 028 9031 0288
web: www.ehsni.gov.uk

Dating from 1618 and refortified in 1652, this is a T-plan house with vaulted rooms. Badly burnt in the early 1800s, this house has remained in ruins.

Times Open at all times.*

COLERAINE

Mount Sandel

☎ 028 9023 0560   🖷 028 9031 0288
web: www.ehsni.gov.uk
dir: 1.25m SSE

This 200ft oval mound overlooking the River Bann is believed to have been fortified in the Iron Age. Nearby is the earliest known inhabited place in Ireland, where post holes and hearths of wooden dwellings, and flint implements dating back to 6650BC have been found. The fort was a stronghold of de Courcy in the late 12th century and was refortified for artillery in the 17th century.

Times Open at all times.* Facilities ℗

DUNGIVEN

Banagher Church

☎ 028 9023 5000   🖷 028 9031 0288
web: www.ehsni.gov.uk
dir: 2m SW

This church was founded by St Muiredach O'Heney in 1100 and altered in later centuries. Today impressive ruins remain. The nave is the oldest part and the square-headed lintelled west door is particularly impressive. Just outside, the perfect miniature stone house, complete with pitched roof and the sculpted figures of a saint at the doorway, is believed to be the tomb of St Muiredach. The saint was said to have endowed his large family with the power of bringing good luck. All they had to do was to sprinkle whoever or whatever needed luck with sand taken from the base of the saint's tomb.

Times Open at all times.* Facilities ℗

DUNGIVEN

Dungiven Priory

☎ 028 9023 5000 🖺 028 9031 0288
web: www.ehsni.gov.uk
dir: SE of town overlooking River Roe

Up until the 17th century Dungiven was the stronghold of the O'Cahan chiefs, and the Augustinian priory, of which extensive ruins remain, was founded by the O'Cahans around 1150. The church, which was altered many times in later centuries, contains one of Northern Ireland's finest medieval tombs. It is the tomb of Cooey na Gall O'Cahan who died in 1385. His sculpted effigy, dressed in Irish armour, lies under a stonework canopy. Below are six kilted warriors.

Times Open Church at all times, chancel only when caretaker available. Check with house at end of lane.* Facilities ℗

LIMAVADY

Rough Fort

☎ 028 7084 8728 🖺 028 7084 8728
e-mail: downhillcastle@nationaltrust.org.uk
web: www.ntni.org.uk
dir: 1m W off A2

Early Christian rath picturesquely surrounded by pine and beech trees, making it a significant landscape feature. The Rough Fort is one of the best examples of an earthwork ring fort in Ireland.

Times Open at all times.* Facilities 🚗 ♿

MAGHERA

Maghera Church

☎ 028 9023 5000   📄 028 9031 0288
web: www.ehsni.gov.uk
dir: E approach to the town

Important 6th-century monastery founded by
St Lurach, later a bishop's see and finally a
parish church. This much-altered church has a
magnificently decorated 12th-century west door.
A cross-carved stone to the west of the church is
supposed to be the grave of the founder.

Times Key from Leisure Centre.* Facilities 🅿

ARDBOE

Ardboe Cross

☎ 028 9023 5000   📄 028 9031 0288
web: www.ehsni.gov.uk
dir: off B73

Situated at Ardboe Point, on the western shore
of Lough Neagh, is the best example of a high
cross to be found in Northern Ireland. Marking
the site of an ancient monastery, the cross has
22 sculpted panels, many recognisably biblical,
including Adam and Eve and the Last Judgment.
It stands over 18ft high and dates back to the
10th century. It is still the rallying place of
the annual Lammas, but praying at the cross
and washing in the lake has been replaced by
traditional music-making, singing and selling
of local produce. The tradition of 'cross reading'
or interpreting the pictures on the cross, is an
honour passed from generation to generation
among the men of the village.

Times Open at all times.* Facilities 🅿

BALLYGAWLEY

U S Grant Ancestral Homestead

Dergenagh Rd BT70 1TW
☎ 028 8555 7133   ▤ 028 8555 7133
e-mail: killymaddy.reception@dungannon.gov.uk
web: www.dungannon.gov.uk
dir: off A4, 2m on Dergenagh road, signed

Ancestral homestead of Ulysses S Grant, 18th
President of the United States of America. The
homestead and farmyard have been restored to
the style and appearance of a mid-19th-century
Irish smallholding. There are many amenities
including a children's play area, purpose built
barbecue and picnic tables and butterfly garden.
Bike hire available (£1/hr).

Times Open all year daily 9-5. Fees Free
admission. Advisable to book in advance for
audio visual show.* Facilities ⓟ ⌱ (outdoor)
⅋ ⊗

BEAGHMORE

Beaghmore Stone Circles and Alignments

☎ 028 9023 5000   ▤ 028 9031 0288
web: www.ehsni.gov.uk

Discovered in the 1930s, these impressive,
ritualistic stones have been dated back to the
early Bronze Age, and may even be Neolithic.
There are three pairs of stone circles, one single
circle, stone rows or alignments and cairns,
which range in height from one to four feet. This
is an area littered with historic monuments,
many discovered by people cutting turf.

Times Open at all times.* Facilities ⓟ

BENBURB

Benburb Castle

☎ 028 9023 5000   📄 028 9031 0288
web: www.ehsni.gov.uk

The castle ruins - three towers and massive walls - are dramatically placed on a cliff-edge 120ft above the River Blackwater. The northwest tower is now restored and has dizzy cliff-edge views. The castle, built by Sir Richard Wingfield around 1615, is actually situated in the grounds of the Servite Priory. There are attractive walks down to the river.

Times Castle grounds open at all times. Special arrangements, made in advance, necessary for access to flanker tower.* Facilities 🅿 ⊗

CASTLECAULFIELD

Castle Caulfield

☎ 028 9023 5000   📄 028 9031 0288
web: www.ehsni.gov.uk

Sir Toby Caulfield, an Oxfordshire knight and ancestor of the Earls of Charlemont, built this manor house in 1619 on the site of an ancient fort. It was badly burnt in 1641, repaired and lived in by the Caulfield/Charlemont family until 1670. It boasts the rare distinction of having had St Oliver Plunkett and John Wesley preach in its grounds. Some fragments of the castle are re-used in the fine, large 17th-century parish church.

Times Open at all times.*

COOKSTOWN

Tullaghoge Fort

☎ 028 9023 5000   🖹 028 9031 0288
web: www.ehsni.gov.uk
dir: 2m S

This large hilltop earthwork, planted with trees, was once the headquarters of the O'Hagans, Chief Justices of the old kingdom of Tyrone. Between the 12th and 16th centuries the O'Neill Chiefs of Ulster were also crowned here - the King Elect was seated on a stone inauguration chair, new sandals were placed on his feet and he was then anointed and crowned. The last such ceremony was held here in the 1590s; in 1600 the stone throne was destroyed by order of Lord Mountjoy.

Times Open at all times.* Facilities ℗

NEWTOWNSTEWART

Harry Avery's Castle

☎ 028 9023 5000   🖹 028 9031 0288
web: www.ehsni.gov.uk
dir: 0.75m SW

The hilltop ruins of a Gaelic stone castle, built around the 14th century by one of the O'Neill chiefs, are the remains of the oldest surviving Irish-built castle in the north. Only the great twin towers of the gatehouse are left. A stairway enables the public to gain access to one of these.

Times Open at all times.* Facilities ⊗ �#

STEWARTSTOWN

Mountjoy Castle

Magheralamfield
☎ 028 9023 5000   📄 028 9031 0288
web: www.ehsni.gov.uk
dir: 3m SE, off B161

Ruins of an early 17th-century brick and stone fort, with four rectangular towers, overlooking Lough Neagh. The fort was built for Lord Deputy Mountjoy during his campaign against Hugh O'Neill, Earl of Tyrone. It was captured and re-captured by the Irish and English during the 17th century and was also used by the armies of James II and William III.

Times Open at all times.* Facilities 🅿

CORK

Cork Public Museum

Fitzgerald Park, Mardyke
☎ 021 4270679   📄 021 4270931
e-mail: museum@corkcity.ie
dir: N of University College

Displays illustrating the history of the city are housed in this museum. The collections cover the economic, social and municipal history from the Mesolithic period onwards. There are fine collections of Cork Silver and Glass.

Times Open all year, Mon-Fri, 11-1 & 2.15-5; Sat 11-1 & 2.15-4; Sun (Apr-Oct only) 3-5.*
Facilities 🅿 🅟 🖵 ♿ toilets for disabled ⊗

BALLYSHANNON

The Water Wheels

Abbey Assaroe

☎ 071 9851580

dir: cross Abbey River on Rossnowlagh Rd, next turning left & follow signs

Abbey Assaroe was founded by Cistercian Monks from Boyle Abbey in the late 12th century, who excelled in water engineering and canalised the river to turn water wheels for mechanical power. Two restored 12th-century mills, one is used as a coffee shop and restaurant; the other houses a small museum related to the history of the Cistercians. Interesting walks in the vicinity with views of the Erne Estuary and Atlantic Ocean.

Times Open May-Oct, daily 10.30-6.30*
Facilities 🅿 Ⓟ 💻 🍴 licensed 🍴 (outdoor) ♿ toilets for disabled shop

DUBLIN

Chester Beatty Library

Dublin Castle

☎ 01 4070750   📄 01 4070760

e-mail: info@cbl.ie

web: www.cbl.ie

dir: 2 min walk from Dame St via the Palace St gate of Dublin Castle, 5 mins from Trinity College

Situated in the city centre, the Chester Beatty Library is an art museum and library which houses the great collection of manuscripts, miniature paintings, prints, drawings, rare books and decorative arts assembled by Sir Alfred Chester Beatty (1875-1968). The exhibitions open a window on the artistic treasures of the great cultures and religions of the world. Egyptian papyrus texts, beautifully illustrated copies of the Qur'an and the Bible, and European medieval and renaissance manuscripts are among the highlights. Turkish and Persian miniatures and striking Buddhist paintings are also on display, as are Chinese dragon robes and Japanese woodblock prints. 2010 is the 10th anniversary of the library moving to Dublin Castle.

Times Open all year, May-Sep, Mon-Fri 10-5; Oct-Apr, Tue-Fri 10-5, Sat 11-5, Sun 1-5. Closed 24-26 Dec, 1 Jan, Good Fri & BH Mons.
Facilities Ⓟ 🍴 licensed ♿ toilets for disabled shop ⊗

DUBLIN

Dublin City Gallery The Hugh Lane

Charlemont House, Parnell Square
☎ 01 2222550 📄 01 8741132
e-mail: info.hughlane@dublincity.ie
web: www.hughlane.ie
dir: Off O'Connell St Parnell Monument. At the top
of Parnell Square

Situated in Charlemont House, a fine Georgian
building, the gallery's collection includes one of
the most extensive collections of 20th-century
Irish art. A superb range of international and
Irish paintings, sculpture, works on paper and
stained glass is also on show. Possibly the most
fascinating aspect of the gallery is Francis
Bacon's Studio, a complete reconstruction of
the painter's studio, and a complete database
of all the items in it. There are public lectures
every Sunday and regular concerts (at noon on
Sundays) throughout the year.

Times Open all year, Tue-Thu 10-6, Fri-Sat 10-5,
Sun 11-5. Closed Mon, Good Fri & 24-25 Dec.*
Facilities ℗ ⯀ & toilets for disabled shop ⊗

DUBLIN

Howth Castle Rhododendron Gardens

Howth
☎ 01 8322624 & 8322256
📄 01 8392405
e-mail: sales@deerpark.iol.ie
dir: 9m NE of city centre, by coast road to Howth.
Before Howth follow signs for Deer Park Hotel

Overlooking the sea on the north side of
Dublin Bay, the rhododendron walks command
spectacular views of the Castle and Ireland's
Eye. The flowers are at their best in May and June.
Visitors should be aware that the gardens are in
some disrepair and the paths somewhat rough
and overgrown in parts.

Times Open all year, daily 8am-dusk. Closed 25
Dec.* Facilities ℗ ⯀ ⦿ licensed & (partly
accessible) (garden unsuitable) toilets for
disabled ⊗

DUBLIN

Irish Museum of Modern Art

Royal Hospital, Military Rd, Kilmainham
☎ 01 6129900   📠 01 6129999
e-mail: info@imma.ie
web: www.imma.ie
dir: 3.5km from city centre, just off N7 opposite Heuston Station

Housed in the Royal Hospital Kilmainham, an impressive 17th-century building, the Irish Museum of Modern Art is Ireland's leading national institution for the collection and presentation of modern and contemporary art. It presents a wide variety of art and artists' ideas in a dynamic programme of exhibitions, which regularly includes bodies of work from the museum's own collection, its award-winning Education and Community Department and the Studio and National Programmes.

Times Please contact Kilmainham Gaol to arrange tours: May-Sep. (Tel: 01 4535984).*
Facilities ❷ ⓟ ⌨ toilets for disabled shop ⊗

DUBLIN

National Gallery of Ireland

Merrion Square
☎ 01 6615133   📠 01 6615372
e-mail: info@ngi.ie
web: www.nationalgallery.ie
dir: N11, M50, follow signs to City Centre

The gallery, founded in 1854 by an Act of Parliament, houses the national collections of Irish art and European Old Masters including Rembrandt, Caravaggio, Poussin, and El Greco. There is also a special room dedicated to Jack B Yeats, and a National Portrait Collection.

Times Open all year, Mon-Sat 9.30-5.30 (Thu 9.30-8.30), Sun 12-5. Closed 24-26 Dec & Good Fri.* Facilities ⓟ ⌨ †⊘ licensed ♿ toilets for disabled shop ⊗

DUBLIN

National Library of Ireland

Kildare St
☎ 01 6030200 🖹 01 6766690
e-mail: info@nli.ie
web: www.nli.ie

Founded in 1877 and based on collections from The Royal Dublin Society. The National Library holds an estimated 8 million items. There are collections of printed books, manuscripts, prints and drawings, photos, maps, newspapers, microfilms and ephemera. Included in the library's collection is the most significant exhibition on the life and works of the 20th century poet WB Yeats. The library's research facilities are open to all those with genuine research needs. In addition to research facilities, services include a regular programme of exhibitions open to the public and Genealogy Service.

Times Open all year, Mon-Wed 9.30-9 (Kildare Street); Thu-Fri 9.30-5. Sat 9.30-1 (reading rooms); 9.30-4.30 (Yeats exhibition). Opening times may vary during public hols. Facilities ℗ ⌨ ♿ toilets for disabled shop ⊗

DUBLIN

National Photographic Archive

Meeting House Square, Temple Bar
☎ 01 6030200 & 6030374 🖹 01 6777451
e-mail: photoarchive@nli.ie
web: www.nli.ie
dir: opposite The Gallery of Photography

The National Photographic Archive, which is part of the National Library of Ireland, was opened in 1998 in an award-winning building in the Temple Bar area of Dublin. The archive holds an unrivalled collection of photographic images relating to Irish history, topography and cultural and social life. The collection is especially rich in late 19th and early 20th-century topographical views and studio portraits, but also includes photographs taken during the Rebellion of 1916 and the subsequent War of Independence and Civil War, as well as other historic events.

Times Open all year, Mon-Fri 10-5, Sat 10-2. (Closed BHs). Facilities ♿ toilets for disabled shop ⊗

DUBLIN

Natural History Museum

Merrion St

☎ 01 6777444 📄 01 6777828

e-mail: education.nmi@indigo.ie

dir: in city centre

The Natural History Museum, which is part of The National Museum of Ireland, is a zoological museum containing diverse collections of world wildlife. The Irish Room, on the ground floor, is devoted largely to Irish mammals, sea creatures and insects. It includes the extinct giant Irish deer and the skeleton of a basking shark. The World Collection, has as its centre piece, the skeleton of a 60ft whale suspended from the roof. Other displays include the Giant Panda and a Pygmy Hippopotamus.

Times Open all year, Tue-Sat 10-5, Sun 2-5. Closed Mon, 25 Dec & Good Fri* Facilities ⓟ ⊗

DUBLIN

Phoenix Park Visitor Centre

Phoenix Park

☎ 01 6770095 📄 01 6726454

e-mail: phoenixparkvisitorcentre@opw.ie

dir: 4km from Dublin

Situated in Phoenix Park, the Visitor Centre provides an historical interpretation of the park from 3500BC, through a series of attractive displays. Part of the building is devoted to nature and there is a colourful film of Phoenix Park. The castle, probably dating from the early 17th century, has been restored to its former glory.

Times Open all year, Nov-mid Mar, Wed-Sun 9.30-5.30; mid Mar-Oct, daily 10-5.45.* Facilities ⓟ ⊑ 🪑 toilets for disabled ⊗

GALWAY

Royal Tara China Gift Centre

Tara Hall, Mervue
☎ 091 705602   📄 091 757574
e-mail: mkilroy@royal-tara.com
web: www.royal-tara.com
dir: N6 from Tourist Office. At rdbt take 2nd left &
at lights turn right

Royal Tara China visitor centre, located minutes
from Galway City Centre, operates from a 17th-
century house situated on five acres.

Times Open all year, Mon-Sat 9-5, Sun 10-5*
Facilities ❷ ♿ toilets for disabled shop ⊗

GORT

Coole Park & Gardens

Coole Nature Reserve
☎ 091 631804   📄 091 631653
e-mail: info@coolepark.ie
web: www.coolepark.ie
dir: 3km N of Gort on N18 Limerick-Galway road,
left turn signed

Once the home of Lady Gregory, dramatist and
co-founder of the Abbey Theatre with W.B. Yeats
and Edward Martyn, now a nature reserve, the
Seven Woods celebrated by Yeats is part of a
nature trail taking in woods and river to Coole
lake. The restored courtyard has a visitor centre
with exhibits and displays of Coole Park's history.
Events around Biodiversity Day in May, and
Heritage week at the end of August.

Times Park Open all year. Visitor Centre Open
Apr-May, daily, 10-5; Jun-Aug, daily, 10-5.*
Facilities ❷ ▯ ⎆ licensed 🃏 (outdoor)
♿ (partly accessible) (visitor centre is fully
accessible. Nature trails are partly accessible.
All main features are accessible) toilets for
disabled ⊗

Roundstone Music, Crafts & Fashion

Craft Centre
☎ 095 35875   📄 095 35980
e-mail: bodhran@iol.ie
web: www.bodhran.com
dir: N59 from Galway to Clifden. After approx 50m turn left at Roundstone sign, 7m to village. Attraction at top of village

The Roundstone Music Craft and Fashion shop is located within the walls of an old Franciscan Monastery. Here you can see Ireland's oldest craft: the Bodhran being made, and regular talks and demonstrations are given. The first RiverDance stage drums were made here and are still on display in the Craftsman's Craftshop. There is an outdoor picnic area in a beautiful location alongside the bell tower by the water where the dolphins swim up to the wall in summer. 2010 is the 30th anniversary of making Bodhrans in Roundstone.

Times Open Apr-Oct 9.30-6, Jul-Sep 9-7, Winter 6 days 9.30-6.* Facilities ℗ ℗ ⊑ 🎋 (indoor & outdoor) ♿ toilets for disabled shop ⊗

KEENAGH

Corlea Trackway Visitor Centre

☎ 043 3322386   📄 043 22442
e-mail: ctrackwayvisitorcentre@opw.ie
dir: off R397, 3km from village, 15km from Longford

The centre interprets an Iron Age bog road which was built in the year 148BC across the boglands close to the River Shannon. The oak road is the largest of its kind to have been uncovered in Europe and was excavated over the years by Professor Barry Raferty of University College Dublin. Inside the building, an 18-metre stretch of preserved road is on permanent display in a specially designed hall with humidifiers to prevent the ancient wood from cracking in the heat.

Times Open early Apr-Sep, daily 10-6.*
Facilities ℗ ⊑ 🎋 toilets for disabled ⊗

MONAGHAN

Monaghan County Museum

1-2 Hill St
☎ 047 82928   ▤ 047 71189
e-mail: comuseum@monghancoco.ie
web: www.monaghan.ie
dir: near town centre, opposite market house
exhibition galleries

This is an award-winning museum of local archaeology, history, arts and crafts. Throughout the year various special exhibitions take place.

Times Open Sep-May, Tue-Fri 10-1 & 2-5 Sat 11-1 & 2-5. Jun-Aug, Mon-Fri 11-5, Thu 11-7, Sat 11-1 & 2-5.* Facilities Ⓟ Ⓧ

WEXFORD

Wexford Wildfowl Reserve

North Slob
☎ 053 9123129   ▤ 053 24785
e-mail: info@heritageireland.ie
dir: 8km NE from Wexford

The reserve is of international importance for Greenland white-fronted geese, Brent geese, Bewick's swans and wigeon. The reserve is a superb place for birdwatching and there are hides and a tower hide available as well as a visitor centre.

Times Open all year, daily 9-5. Other hours by arrangement with the warden. Closed 25 Dec. Notice on gate if reserve closed.* Facilities Ⓟ 🛋 toilets for disabled Ⓧ